IT'S GOT TO BE
RIGHT HERE SOMEWHERE

IT'S GOT TO BE RIGHT HERE SOMEWHERE

ROY F. CHALKER, SR.

THE TRUE CITIZEN, INC.
WAYNESBORO, GEORGIA

Published by
THE TRUE CITIZEN, INC.
610 Academy Avenue, Waynesboro, Georgia 30830

Manufactured in the United States of America

Edited and Designed by Jimmy E. Bennett

Library of Congress Catalog Card No. 85-51935

Other Titles by Roy F. Chalker:
An All Day Hanging and Dinner on the Ground, 1982

To Mae

Author's Note

Late in 1982, we published *An All Day Hanging and Dinner on the Ground,* which was a compilation of newspaper columns and short stories I had written over several years. Frankly, the reception was better than we had expected; four months later it was necessary to put it through another printing. Since that time we have received hundreds of expressions favorable to the book, and many of you have asked me to write another.

It takes a little while. As you know, many of you identify with the events included in these stories. They belong to you as well as to me. The articles and stories usually need to be "prompted" by something, or somebody. I am sorry it has taken three years.

Several readers said our first book is the kind of book you want to keep permanently. Others have bought copies for children so they may carry these stories on into another generation or two. Many have ordered copies for presents to kinsmen who might otherwise miss it.

The present book, *It's Got to be Right Here Somewhere,* is very much a continuation of *An All Day Hanging ...;* they are companions.

And you might like to know that I wrote this book with you in mind.

Roy F. Chalker

Contents

1

FATHERS ARE NOT SUPPOSED TO CRY

2

IT'S GOT TO BE RIGHT HERE SOMEWHERE

3

FAMILY REUNION TIME

4

5

6

7

8

9

10

11

1

FATHERS ARE NOT SUPPOSED TO CRY

The most frustrating behavior I know is the stand-off, reserve and formality that often exists between fathers and older sons.

Keepin' Company

For two long years Martha sat alone, mourning her husband of 30 years. It was then that Tobe had asked Martha's brother to ask her if she would mind if he called on her.

Everybody knew Tobe — dear, gentle Toby, as they all called him. Martha was glad to have the company. And, what harm could there be?

The community was glad to hear the news; two of the most respected elders were keepin' company.

At a regular hour every Sunday evening, Tobe came over in his buggy, hitched his horse to the fence and cautiously made his way up the garden walk. Martha, neat as a pin with her hair combed tight and balled in the back, wearing a dress-up apron, would usually meet him at the door.

Hello, Martha. Howdy, Toby, and won't you have a seat over here in the shade. Thank you, Martha; I believe I will. How have you been — and on and on. They talked of the weather; of the neighbors; of the crops; of the nieces and nephews. Sometimes they discussed the sermons each had heard that morning in their respective churches.

Usually, Martha served tea or lemonade and a bit of cake that Toby declared each time to be "the best" he had ever eaten. Sometimes, Toby brought ice cream.

The flowers might bloom all over the world and romance might run rampant in other climes, but companionship held sway on their front porch to Martha and Tobe. And, neither touched the other beyond a proper handshake of welcome and good-bye. Each learned to look forward to their meeting and occasionally was heard to say, "I'll remember to mention that to Toby (or Martha) come Sunday."

Often, they sat in silence and listened to the birds or crickets, the barking of a dog or the lowing of some distant cow. They felt no compulsion to fill every minute with words. It was enough to feel the presence of the other. They shared memories of happiness and sadness, of the great and the trivial and spoke of those who had gone before. There was no embarrassment at mentioning their departed mates. Each knew the other's feelings and respected them.

Time went by, neither fast nor slow. Martha became quieter and sometimes forgetful. Toby staggered a little as he came up the walk and held carefully to the bannister of the steps. The pleasure of their company was unabated, however, and their visits went on as regularly as the seasons.

Perhaps it would make a better story if it could be reported that their visits resulted in some degree of romance — or finally, marriage. But, such was not the case.

Martha and Toby gradually grew more infirm. Sometimes, weeks went by with the front porch empty. Then, one would have to visit the other in the hospital or at the sickbed.

When the word finally came that Toby had gone on, Martha was too old to completely understand that she had taken an everlasting leave of her old and agreeable companion. Some said she would often ask if Toby was waiting for her.

They are both gone now. The birds and the crickets sing alone. The cow's lowing goes unheard. Occasionally, a passing neighbor remembers and looks toward where Martha and Toby kept company on Sunday afternoons — and thinks of the wonders of simple companionship.

Fathers are not Supposed to Cry

The most frustrating behavior I know of is the stand-off, reserve and formality that often exists between fathers and older sons.

Perhaps there is a reason for it, but I can't imagine what it could be.

Why can't a father put an arm around the shoulders of his son as he may a daughter?

Why is there a barrier that keeps some sons from showing affection for their fathers?

Many years ago I watched as a family saw an older son aboard a military airplane, leaving for a battle zone.

The mother and son embraced, and, of course, mother was crying.

Sister held her brother close and gave him love pats

on the shoulder and shed her pent up tears.

All the time, dad was standing an arm's length away, half holding out his empty arms and shifting from one foot to the other. His son glanced at him off and on as if he knew they were both leaving something undone.

I wanted to cry out, "Hug your dad, too. He loves you." I wanted to say, "Pop, before it's too late, grab him to you."

But the opportunity for expression of warmth and understanding had passed. The son stuck out his hand for a quick shake and a half-mumbled, "good bye, dad."

Just too late, dad reached out and brushed his shoulder, self-consciously.

Mother and sister clung to the soldier as long as they could. Pop just stood there and rubbed his thumbs and fingers together. His lips were forming words that couldn't get past a full heart.

When the young soldier finally rushed up the ramp, mother and sister were holding handkerchiefs to their eyes, but dad was just standing there by himself, waving and drinking in hungrily what he knew might be the last glimpse he would ever have of his son.

You had to look close to see that his shoulders were shaking with sobs.

Fathers are not supposed to cry, either.

They Passed Him by on the Other Side

T here used to be a black man who hung around town and begged for "a little help." He usually had the odor of wine or whiskey. Most of the time he sat or leaned on something and was a perfect picture of what was considered "sorry."

You know: sorry, no good, lazy. Just another wino, panhandling to keep from working.

Most people avoided him; couldn't stand to hear him whine that he drank a little to ease the pain. When somebody offered him "a little work," he would whimper that he wasn't able. In disgust, they would leave him empty-handed.

He was around for several years. Then people started noticing his absence. Somebody asked whatever happened to him. Was he in jail or something?

No. He had "up and died."

"You mean he was really sick?"

"Yes, sir. He lived in a lot of pain. Finally the government put on a program. He got examined, but it was too late.

"No, sir. He wasn't lying. The government doctors said he had Sickle Cell Anemia; slow; painful; no help."

And, all who had passed him by hung our heads.

Desperation Years

T here comes a time in the lives of many people when they feel that the boat is about to leave them standing on the shore by themselves. In their frantic desperation to catch on or hold on, they do things, think things and say things that in other years they might look upon as somewhat excessive.

It is what makes some old men buy yellow convertible automobiles, try to wear college-boy fashions, take scalp treatments and change their spectacles for contact lenses. If they are single, they sometimes act silly around young ladies. If they are married, their wives may have to snatch them back to their senses.

It is what makes old ladies pour hair dye down their collars, wear dresses that would better become their daughters, gush themselves silly around young men, and go to health spas to try to recapture their youth. They sometimes have their faces lifted along with everything else that has drooped.

Of course, the great majority who survive these years of frantic desperation are the good and quiet people who were born with enough sense and character and who have enough God-given grace to carry them through.

Sometimes, the more desperate talk faster and faster, personally and on the telephone, as if their conversation could control the situation and make time stand still. It is somewhat akin to whistling in the dark.

Nothing said here is intended to discourage those

who try to look their best, or who sensibly seek a commensurate companionship among those of their kind. But, people who have lived long enough to earn their dignity should not easily shuffle it away.

All times are good times, if we but learn how to make the most of them.

2

IT'S GOT TO BE RIGHT HERE SOMEWHERE

In no other game that uses a ball is the loss of a ball of less lasting consequence than in the game of golf ... But, I have discovered that there is a rather large school of us who can't stand the trauma of losing a golf ball.

The Hog Calling Lady

Head shrinkers, concerned citizens and just ordinary folks are always talking about what failure and defeat do to the human spirit. It is said such disappointment starts early and causes some babies to spit up or require security blankets.

Perhaps you have seen cases where there is evidence that some terrible blight has taken out after some folks. They've got that look of impending doom written all over their faces. They seek out recognition by dressing like freaks; and some go too long between washing and delousing, so they may console one another by saying the power structure acts as if it thinks they stink.

They are usually very defensive and they carry their portable ongoing arguments around with them.

But, this is not the subject I intended. It was my purpose to write about *success* which often results in the undoing of otherwise good-to-middlin' folks.

For instance, there was once a nice lady who looked fairly good and who had ensconced herself into the life of her community by attending church, both the morning and the night shift, serving as a sub-chairperson of the Girl Scout cookie drive and by forwarding the local gossip to the next regular recipient.

Like I said, the woman was doing all right. But, she made the mistake of entering the ladies' hog-calling contest at the local county fair. She won the blue ribbon. Then, with diligence and hard application, and by neglecting her family, she worked herself up to the state finals.

There were many good hog-callers, but this lady threw in a natural clincher — when she had screamed the wail, she lowered her voice into a grunt and said "pig, pig, pig" in rapid succession.

Well, that did it. Pandemonium broke loose in the hog exhibit tent. A half-dozen male hogs tore down their fence and two of the judges fell off of the platform.

Naturally, she won first, second and third places and there was a big argument about also giving her two honorable mentions.

As you already may have guessed, the honor and recognition turned this lady away from ordinary domestic pursuits. Thenceforth, she felt the necessity of hauling herself around in a panel truck with her name emblazoned on all four sides and written in reverse on the front — like ambulance spelled backwards.

She became famous in the hog-calling circuits, and when there were no events at which she might exhibit her talents, she would go downtown in her little community, and, at the most unexpected times, local citizens and passing strangers would be startled out of their tracks by her sudden screech and wail, followed by a throaty "pig, pig, pig."

She had become addicted to it. She needed the recognition. She craved the honor.

Her husband and children gradually withdrew from society. They stopped eating bacon for breakfast, and the husband admitted he "couldn't look a pork chop in the face."

Sometimes this strange conduct starts early:

There was the case of the little girl who came running home to release the bulletin that she "had just been elected 'Miss Remedial Reading' of the lower fourth grade."

Honor had come and she was on her way.

For Too Long

For too long, prominent-featured women have tended to overdo the contour styles in clothing. The trend started many years ago when styles started following the skin. Very recently, we have seen tops and blue jeans that appear to have been spray-painted onto the wearer.

But, speaking of sweaters only: I vividly recall an unknown young lady in a nearby city who walked down the street at the same time every day, wearing the same style sweater. She was, to speak plainly, very shapely.

She did not walk smoothly, resulting in considerable movement of some of her better features — both front and back, up and down.

Of course, this was not entirely unusual. The uniqueness involved was the fact that some of her features did not maintain their rhythm together. They took turns.

She walked the downtown full six blocks, as I have said, at the same time, every day.

As you might imagine, she was noticed. In fact, men and boys started taking their coffee breaks and lunch hours to coincide with the event. They lined the sidewalk on each side, shoulder-to-shoulder; all second and third-floor windows were permanently reserved for that time; the local Air Force base changed its flight patterns and flew low; there was talk of recessing school in the upper grades.

I do not know what happened to the young lady, but I've always assumed that something did.

But, the above was not my primary subject:

The hopeful sign that has appeared recently is the new move to more loose-fitting clothing; a style that appeals to the curiosity and the exploratory nature of man; something to put the mystery back into the business at hand.

It would seem to be a movement with a great future.

It's Got To Be
Right Here Somewhere

I n no other game that uses a ball is the loss of a ball of less lasting consequence than in the game of golf.

I know this and you know this.

But, I have discovered that there is a rather large school of us who can't stand the trauma of losing a golf ball.

For a few years I played only spasmodically because of this personality fixation. I was reluctant to mention it around, because I realize that there is the distant probability that there are those who will think I'm miserly in the matter.

I have waited until I could find some validating associations of like but more distinguished standing. In other words, somebody who can afford to lose a dollar-and-a-half ball. I've found such gentlemen:

The late John D. Rockefeller Sr. hired two caddies to ensure that he suffered no loss in that department. He paid them the going price and presumably tipped them a dime. But, sad the day and absent was the dime if a ball remained lost.

A more recent example was the late Mr. Kresge, owner of the K-Mart chain. He was an ultra-multi-millionaire who was famed for his generosity and philanthropy. It is sadly reported that he tried the game of golf and immediately gave it up, because he could not stand to lose a ball.

These are just two examples, but I am convinced that there are many more in the same category who might have grown great in the game, but were stopped cold by some concealing clump of grass or clod of clay. The number may be greater than suspected.

In spite of the urging of fellow players and those people back there, trying to come through, I have perfected a system for recouping lost balls.

I have five methods:

There is the application-of-logic method. I pick the area that it could not possibly be in and the spot that it might most likely be and I work between them.

Then there is the farming method. Divide a section of the course up into imaginary rows. Take it a row at a time. This works if you take in enough territory to start with and if you brought a snack to tide you over.

The Easter egg method is faster but less rewarding. You just check under the clumps of grass large enough to hide a ball.

The rake method is very thorough. You take a club in each hand and rake every inch of ground for miles around. You don't always find the ball you lost, but quite often you come up with balls lost previously by less concerned players.

This last method for finding lost golf balls, I am reluctant to mention until I can get it patented. It is the To-Heck-With-It approach. You start walking off like you don't really care, but all the time you are scrutinizing semi-surreptitiously in all directions. You are hoping that your devil-may-care attitude may elicit the aid of dame fortune so that you may not go away empty handed, as it were.

I have mentioned the dollar-and-a-half ball. I did so

merely to give a point of reference. It is not true that everybody plays every game with brand new $1.50 balls. The fact is, very few people are so extravagant or daring. The flagrant use of expensive new balls in every round is confined pretty well to parvenu and tournament players. Most of the rest of us use what are known as "dime balls." They are balls picked up by caddies and greens workers. They are usually sliced or three-cornered or water-soaked or something.

One might think that losing a dime ball should cause no considerable concern. Such is not the case. The price of the ball has little to do with it.

It's just knowing that "it's got to be right here somewhere" and feeling the challenge to find it.

By the time one has exhausted the better part of the day searching and seeking, the zest for the game has passed and one is wont to skip a hole or two and return to the soothing shelter.

I am convinced that this is one of the greatest impediments to the national sport. Something should be done about it.

I merely mention it, but what about a Lost Ball Anonymous Association?

(Author's Note: If any of the above was stolen, including golf balls, the offended have my apologies.)

3

FAMILY REUNION TIME

If you weren't there, it's your own fault. You know good and well that the family reunion always comes on the Sunday closest to the third Friday at Grandpa's place

Family Reunion Time

I f you weren't there, it's your own fault. You know good and well that the family reunion always comes on the Sunday closest to the third Friday at Grandpa's place.

It's been going on since nobody remembers when. Grandpa always barbecues a hog and furnishes the paper plates, plastic forks, etc., and his old maid daughter makes the tea, making it too strong and too sweet. Everybody else brings a basket of fried chicken, Irish 'tater salad and a variety of cakes.

Cousin Mae always brings a great big bowl of heavenly hash; the darndest mess-and-glom you ever saw, but good, nevertheless.

The last gathering brought folks from as far away as Pawtucket, and that is about as far as you can get. The menfolks stand out under the trees and talk about olden times, and the womenfolks gather in the house and talk about everybody, including the younguns — the yard-runners, the porch walkers, the crawlers and the lap-babies.

Some of the cousins stand around, looking dumb; some look superior and some have inferiority complexes and some are just plain.

Some of the menfolks are nippin' and some nappin' and all of them are impatient for the dinner. One cousin-in-law is a part-time preacher who will be called on to "say a few words."

Two or three of the in-law wives are trying to be insulted so they can spend the next 12 months "being hurt" at some loud-mouth but innocent talker.

Older folks are saying things like, "Well, I see you're still holding up right on" and "you aren't showin' your age."

When the blessing gets said, the men stand back, bashful, and wait for the wives to go get it for them. Everybody goes by and says, "I sure want a piece of Aunt Minnie's pie. It's always good." You know, courteous things like that.

Then Grandpa says some of the same old things, and all the way-out folks come by and hug him until he gets plumb tired of it.

The preacher-in-law finally says "a few words" and everybody says what a nice fellow he is. After another "settin down" visit, everybody starts scrambling around to get their stuff back in the baskets and boxes, and some start to asking about their lost spoons, etc. Then everybody tells everybody else goodbye at least 14 times. And, there is a lot of huggin' and pattin', and everybody gradually leaves, only to return again next year.

Dippin' Snuff

S ome people have asked what young folks did to fill their time before radio, record players and television destroyed the tranquility.

Those who can remember well beyond 50 years may recall that young people spent most of the weekdays doing chores around the house, like cutting and toting stove wood; watering and feeding the chickens, cows and mules or horses; running errands, etc.

On the less constructive side, they played ball, marbles and mumblepeg. Girls played jump-the-rope (hot peas), hide-and-seek and other sissy stuff like that.

Boys built kites, using dog fennels for the frame, old newspapers for cover and flour-and-water paste to hold it together.

With the games and the chores, along with school, the weekdays were pretty well filled. It was Sunday afternoons that were lonesome.

Sunday mornings were busy with everybody getting bathed, dressed and shoe-shined for church. After Sunday dinner, the older folks dozed on the porch while the children and teenagers looked for something to do.

If you lived in a little town, you strolled down to the drugstore, it being about the only establishment that could be open on Sunday afternoons without the owner going to hell.

When you had spent your nickel, if you had one, sometimes you could get up a small group of boys and walk out to the edge of town where the bridge crossed the creek. Sometimes you leaned over the rail and dropped rocks in the water and watched them splash. All the time, everybody took turns wishing, wishing for someplace to go and some kind of big car to go in — like a Maxwell or a Hudson or a Studebaker. Yes sir, someday we were going to come back and split that little old town wide open with a big fancy car.

If you were required to stay around the neighborhood Sunday afternoons, you could lie on your back on the roof of the cowshed and look up at the clouds and the birds passing over and wish you could fly like that.

Sometimes you could aggravate cats by dangling string down on their faces while they were trying to sleep.

When things were really sho-nuff dull, you could get off to one side and watch an old lady, in her apron and bonnet, rub her Railroad McAboy snuff on her teeth with a little snuff-stick, while she was in prayerful thought.

Like I say, things had to be pretty dull when you found it interesting to watch an old lady dip snuff.

But, on the other hand, I'll bet you the world is full of folks who have never had the opportunity to watch a little old lady enjoy her snuff without being pestered to death by some rock group.

Scald and Scour

B etcha haven't heard of anybody "scalding and scouring" recently.

Fifty or so years ago, almost nobody had wall-to-wall carpets. Most folks felt themselves pretty lucky if they had wall-to-wall floors. Back then, when a family had a contagious disease, or prepared to move into another house they found dirty, they would scald and scour. That meant boiling washpots full of water with strong lye soap and then scrubbing floors and walls with corn-shuck mops, followed by rinsing with more scalding fresh water.

If somebody had moved out of a house and the new tenants found it necessary to scald and scour, the folks who had left the house dirty got "talked about" something scandalous. It was a terrible reflection on their habits and character.

The conversation went something like this: "They tell me you had to scald and scour before you could move in?" The answer would be: "Yes, we shore did. All I got to say is that was a filthy bunch. They must have fed hogs in the living room."

Sometimes, if there was a city hall or courthouse fight, some candidate would promise to "throw the rascals out and then I'm gonna scald and scour." This was good for a laugh and maybe votes.

Many families did a thorough job of cleaning their own houses a couple of times a year. They would drag furniture outdoors and use the corn shuck mops and everybody had to eat on the porch while the house dried out.

Nowadays, of course, all those folks who can't use a vacuum on their carpet use a neat little mop that squeezes itself.

We have become so dainty!

Good Eatin'

An old friend and I were recently talking about the best things we had ever eaten. We never settled the discussion, but the following were mentioned prominently:

Warm egg-bread with fried streak-o-lean.

The first "mess of fresh" at hog killing time.

Real honest-to-goodness, slow pit-cooked barbecue.

Sardines and Johnny cakes, eaten on the back counter of a country store.

Cold potato pie and buttermilk, along about midnight.

Charcoaled ground-round with a big slice of Vidalia onion — enjoyed with neighbors on Saturday night.

One and one-half inch thick, good steak — charcoaled, on special occasions.

Warm spiced apple pie with melted cheese (reaffirms your patriotism better than a loyalty oath).

Smother-fried quail, grits, gravy and hot biscuits — eaten with friends.

Fried lace-edged cornbread and cold milk — eaten surreptitiously.

Fried fish, hushpuppies and hot coffee — eaten on

the banks of a creek, with fishing buddies, about two hours late.

Flapjacks, ribbon cane syrup, chips of cured ham and hot coffee — eaten on a cold morning.

Rat trap cheese and soda crakers, with a big orange drink — after a long, hot walk.

Homemade, hand-turned lemon ice cream, served on the back porch Sunday afternoon — with "company."

'Scuse me. Let's go get a bite to eat.

4

STANDIN' IN THE NEED

Nobody messes with the subject of prayer. If he does, he gets into trouble — with everybody; maybe even the Lord.

Standin' in the Need

Nobody messes with the subject of prayer. If he does, he gets into trouble — with everybody; maybe even the Lord.

First and foremost, you make trouble with the hyprocrites, many of whom think the Lord can be soft-soaped with a lot of thees, thous and thines.

Second, there are the on-again-off-again suppliants who live like sinners 'til an emergency comes along. Then they're ready to "make a deal;" like the man in the falling aeroplane: "Lord, if You'll get me safely down, I'll give You half of everything I've got." When he gets down, he makes the Lord "a better deal: If I ever go up again, I'll give it all to You."

Then, there are those who believe the Lord needs "bringing up to date." They pray for a change. The prayer turns out to be an accusation that the Lord doesn't know how to handle His business or is not handling it as He should.

Also, we always have the Jeeter Lester type: "Lord, I've done told You, now. I'm gonna give You one more chance, then I'm gonna take things into my own hands."

Then, there are the adversaries: All combat troops, on all sides, believe that "God is on our side." Both sides in a ball game ask the Lord to join them: "Let's give 'em hell, Lord."

In some countries, the local brand of religion permits the erection of "prayer wheels" by the side of roads so that the traveler can reach over and spin the wheel. As the wheel turns, the supplicant expects credits for each round. Some of the more devout build prayer wheels which are powered by windmills. There are no computers to keep an accounting. The Lord is expected to keep up with the total and credit it under customary accounting practices.

There are some like the old man who prayed in a loud voice, but rubbed a rabbit's foot at the same time: "I ain't takin' no chances."

There are those of little faith like the chaplain of the ship in a storm, who asked the captain, "How bad is it?" The reply was, "We're in the hands of the Lord." The distressed chaplain's comment was, "I didn't know it was that bad."

There is an unselfish type of prayer as was offered up by the fellow caught out on a limb by a bear: "Lord, if You can't help me, please don't help the bear."

And, of course, everybody has heard about the prayer of the little mouse: "Lord, I don't care for any more cheese; just help me get out of this trap."

(None of the above should discourage anyone from "having a little talk with the Lord when he's standin' in the need of prayer.")

The Colonel and the Deacon

The Colonel was retired; always had been. He had been called *Colonel* ever since Ole Gene had put him on the Governor's staff. He was one of about 7,000 at the time.

The deacon was the best boat paddler in the community, except for the fact that he paddled from the front end of the boat; said he "wasn't gonna set in the back seat of nothing."

The two went together like salt and pepper. The Colonel furnished everything but the bait and divided the fish at the end of the day, plus the short half of a Ball Mason jar of refreshments. They had been fishing companions for a lifetime. The Colonel preferred quietness, but he had grown accustomed to not always getting it. Either one's opinion was about as good as the other's, but the deacon used the Colonel to bounce off his ruminations.

"Colonel, what's all this I hear the folks in the churches are arguing about; what's near-yancy?"

"You mean inerrancy."

"What's that mean?"

"It means some folks say everybody has got to believe exactly what they believe the Bible means — or they are certain to go to hell."

"Shonuff?"

The deacon scratched his head to stimulate cogitation: "Well, that's what our preacher meant, I reckon. T'other night a sister spoke out and said, 'Preacher, we all believe in the Bible, but some few do say they don't know what it means in places. Preacher, just what does it mean — exactly'?"

The preacher's mouth fell open as he looked at the sister: "Here it is," and he slapped it on the cover as he added, "It means what it means." The sister dropped into her seat and everybody said "Amen."

"But, I'm a deacon and I don't know what I'm supposed to believe; I don't know nothin' about this near-yancy."

They fished several spots before the deacon broke the silence, again. He finally said, "It's just like everything else; some folks demand that you believe what they believe — or else.

"My sister lives in a little place down below Ludowici. They ain't got 50 people in the whole town, countin' hound dogs and chickens, but they got two separate churches. One bunch believes Pharaoh's daughter found Moses in the bullrushes while the other bunch believes that's 'just *her* story'. So, they all split up.

"Colonel, ain't it about time to pass that fruit jar around again?"

If it is Written There

I doubt that you will often find it now. Things have changed so, but it used to be the most prominent thing in the home. It rested on a center table in the "front room" (or parlor, if you were among the well-to-do).

The Family Bible, I mean.

Every member of the family knew about the Family Bible. They might come and go; might be flippant or strict about anything else, but every kith and kin, whether he read it or not, stood in awe and respect of the Family Bible. Nothing promised on it was ever treated lightly.

It was a big book. "Holy Bible" was stamped in ornate gold leaf letters on its spine and cover. There was a page near the front that said "Presented To _____, By _____."

There was a full color picture of Moses, holding the Ten Commandments, followed by maps of the Holy Land. Of course, all the illustrations and study helps were there.

In every Family Bible there was a special section for Marriages, Births, Deaths and Family Memoranda. These pages were filled in with careful penmanship; with happiness or sadness, as the occasion warranted, but always with reverence and honesty.

Modern cynicism has destroyed many things; moral laxity allows for many questions, but, if you have had need of proof of births, deaths and marriages 50, 60 and more years ago, and have been able to present an old Family Bible to some governmental agency, then you know how satisfying it is to hear the answer:

"Oh yes, if it is written there, it is proof without question."

And, for those whose faith is sometimes tattered and torn, there is a comfort here.

Were You There?

Many people have spoken of their memories of certain hymns — almost all of us have our favorites. Some of us have lived long enough to remember events of "all day singing and dinner on the ground," where an entire congregation started early and finished late.

They would sing until they were hoarse or until their "voices limbered up," then they would recess to eat from outdoor tables under the shade of the trees. After a visit and a short rest, they would continue the afternoon session.

Most folks have a special church in their memories, and when they hear the playing and singing of an old favorite, it takes them back. Many remember a modest, austere church associated with their parents or grandparents. Sometimes they are surprised to find that so many others have had the same experience.

Often the haunting strains of a remembered hymn hover over a small congregation at some Wednesday night service at which souls were moved by such as *Precious Mem'ries* ... "Unseen angels, sent from somewhere to my soul ... how they linger," sung by voices seasoned by sorrow and drudgery, coming together in a common faith and love.

Or, "What a privilege to carry everything to God in prayer" in *What A Friend We Have In Jesus*, "all our sins and griefs to bear."

Amazing Grace, sung in the proper setting, has raised goose bumps that are remembered to this day.

Rock of Ages has been a favorite of many for its 150 years.

The Old Rugged Cross is of recent times. It was written in 1913, but may be the all-time favorite ... "On a hill far away."

When The Roll Is Called Up Yonder; "when the trumpet of the Lord shall sound and time shall be no more."

In The Garden; "I come to the garden alone — while the dew is still on the roses."

Perhaps you have had the privilege of hearing a black congregation which loved the Lord and enjoyed worshiping Him in song: *Were You There When They Crucified My Lord?;* "Oh, sometimes it causes me to tremble, tremble, tremble. Were you there ... ?"

Of course, *In The Sweet By And By* was one of the favorites of all of us. "... We shall meet on that beautiful shore ..."

Will The Circle Be Unbroken ... "in the sky, Lord, in the sky?"

He's Got The Whole World In His Hands ... "He's got you and me, brother."

Just A Closer Walk With Thee ... "Let it be, Blessed Lord, Let it be."

I Believe ... "that somewhere in the darkest night a candle glows."

Sweet Hour Of Prayer, Beyond The Sunset, It Is No Secret What God Can Do and *Whispering Hope* have become classics.

I Am Bound For The Promised Land ... "On Jordan's stormy banks I stand ..."

When They Ring Those Golden Bells. The author of this one was at one time a clown in the Barnum and

Bailey Circus, but his hymn has brought spiritual comfort to millions. "There's a land beyond the river ..."

Softly And Tenderly. It is said that the great evangelist Dwight Moody, on his death bed, told the author, Will Thompson, "Will, I would rather have written 'Softly And Tenderly, Jesus Is Calling' than anything I've been able to do in my whole life."

Several years ago, a survey was conducted to determine the most popular hymns. At that time, including the above favorites, were:

The Old Rugged Cross, How Great Thou Art, What A Friend We Have In Jesus, In The Garden, Amazing Grace;

Rock Of Ages, Sweet Hour Of Prayer, Abide With Me, Beyond The Sunset, Whispering Hope;

Just A Closer Walk With Thee, A Mighty Fortress, Nearer My God To Thee, God Will Take Care Of You, Have Thine Own Way;

Just As I Am, Onward Christian Soldiers, The Lord's Prayer, Were You There?, Blessed Assurance;

I Believe, I Need Thee Every Hour, Lead Kindly Light, Will The Circle Be Unbroken?, Near The Cross;

Jesus, Lover Of My Soul, Faith Of Our Fathers, Holy, Holy, Holy, Beautiful Isle Of Somewhere, Beautiful Garden Of Prayer;

Take Time To Be Holy, When The Roll Is Called Up Yonder, I Love To Tell The Story, In The Sweet By And By, Great Is Thy Faithfulness.

5

CLEARING NEW GROUND

We were a farm family. We didn't live on the farm at the time. We were inclined that way, but we just couldn't afford the luxury then.

Thoughts of a Frustrated Farmer

Jim was sitting where he could look out over his land. Some of the land he had inherited; some had belonged to Jennie's family; some he had bought when land was cheap; and some he had paid way too much for at a time when he and most everybody else thought you "had to expand or go out of business."

With more land you had to have more equipment to work it. The land justified more equipment and more equipment justified more land. When you planted it, you had to fertilize it; when you fertilized it, you had to protect your investment with cultivation — insecticides, gasoline, diesel fuel, irrigation and a dozen other expenses most people didn't know about.

When you got hooked into a crop the gamble got bigger every day and there was nothing you could do but keep on "anteing up."

You could blame it on dry years, high interest and the economy. But, Jim felt right then you could blame it all on a no-win game. Even when you made good

crops, it worked to drive prices down to a losing pro-
position.

Like most of his fellow farmers, he had massaged his
mind with the thought somebody had to feed the world
and the American farmer was elected. All the risk and
worry he had donated was for a noble cause. That was
probably true, but, right now, that noble cause was letting Jim worry about Jim. He was the one looking at
bankruptcy.

He had worried until he was sick. The government
had helped — or tried to help — and had helped him
in deeper.

He had even thought briefly about suicide; that
would save him embarrassment and the trauma of seeing his home and land go in a foreclosure sale. But,
that would leave it all on Jennie and the children,
which was no solution.

Sometimes he felt like a fool; like a compulsive
gambler, just remembering how he had risked
everything on another turn of the wheel. But, he was
not alone. He had acted upon the best advice available
at the time. A lot more good men had done exactly the
same thing. If misery wanted company, he had plenty.
He might be broke ... he wasn't lonesome.

Maybe starting over wouldn't be all bad. At least he
might lay down some of his burdens. It would mean
getting a job; giving up most things and living leaner.
The kids might have to work their way through college,
or commute to a nearby junior college or technical
school.

There were a lot of adjustments he hated to think
about right now. Giving up the land and their home
was hard to ponder, but there were times now when

the land he loved had begun to look more like a dream which had turned into a nightmare. Losing it all wouldn't be all bad. He knew of dozens more who were in the same boat. They would find a way. It wasn't as if he were a failure or that they were failures; there was something wrong with a system which was defeating an entire industry.

If the government knew what to do to remedy the situation, it had better get busy.

For Jim and a lot of others, it was already too late.

Fading Farm Sounds

F or those whose memories are long and whose early years were spent on the farm, there are sounds that linger:

The squeak of a well pulley; mules gnawing corn in their stalls; the groan of a lot gate; the bouncing rattle of a wagon body; the peep of little chicks; the grunt of a hog; the low mooing of cattle on the way to be milked; the anxious whinney of a horse; the rattle of a loose piece of tin roofing; the bump of a plow stock;

The chime of trace chains being unloosed; the scurry of rats when the corn crib door is opened; the swish of corn being run through the sheller; the flop made by the harness as it was swung up on the horses or mules; the last squeal of a pig being slaughtered; the farmer's rough but reassuring voice giving orders to his team;

The agitated cackling of poultry scurrying out of the way; the early morning frying of ham or streak-o-lean and the pouring of coffee; the promise of a wall-mounted coffee grinder; the splitting of stove wood for the kitchen; the bump of an oak bucket against the well curb;

The rhythmic dropping of seed from a one-row, Ledbetter corn planter; the drop of a bale of hay from the loft; hens singing in their contentment, and cackling when leaving their nest; roosters crowing at daybreak; the irregular sharpening noise of the grind stone; the hand-patting of biscuits in a bread tray; singing crickets at early night; and the gentle squeak of the porch swing.

Goats and Gourds

Perry Winkle, one of the leading farmers in Hedgerow County, started off like almost everybody else in that profession — just a little behind the eight-ball.

Perry worked hard, used modern cultivation practices, kept abreast of current agricultural methods, indulged in "intensive farming" — and lost his shirt.

He was dejected and had a bad case of the mullygrubbs. He decided to go and talk to his grandpa and see if he knew what he had been doing wrong.

"Gramps, I've been doing all the good things and I still can't win ... almost two bales of cotton to the acre; a bumper crop of soys and I am still backing up. What's the matter?"

Gramps had retained that nervous jump and washed

out look left over from the Great Depression. He couldn't roll his own Prince Albert cigarette without spilling a little; same way with his toddy. It didn't stop him from having an opinion, though.

"Son, this situation ain't nothing new to me. I went through the same thing in the Great Depression. I made 10 bushels of corn to the acre and got 35 cents a bushel. That comes to $3.50 gross per acre, if you recollect. I made one bale of cotton for every three or four acres, and, when I was lucky I got 10 cents a pound. That's $50. And, you had to plant it and plow it and chop it and fertilize it when you could afford to. And, you had to walk around and cuss while the weevil ate it up. Then you hand-picked what was left.

"If you were lucky, you had a garden and raised your own meat part of the year. When you ran out, you bought fatback for 8 cents and 10 cents a pound.

"The harder we farmed, the more we lost.

"Son, when the going gets hard and you can't win for losing, you don't need to do more of whatever it is you are doing; you need to do less; you don't need to do that intensive farming; what you need to do is dee-fensive farming.

"Of course, my dollars then were like your 20s now. You handle a lot more money than I did, but, percentage-wise you get to keep about the same and that adds up to minus in both instances.

"Sometimes you can get too efficient: Why just 'tother day, I saw one of those efficiency experts stand-ing at the entrance of one of those big government buildings. He wouldn't let anybody use the revolving door until a group of four people was assembled.

"I don't know what to tell you to do, but one year,

back when things got so bad, I quit raising anything but goats and gourds.

"Didn't make a dime that year, but I didn't lose anything either."

Timing and Potential

W hen a farmer plants a seed to develop in its proper season, by his timing he increases its potential for harvest.

Too early or too late for the climate, too early or too late for the harvest, too early or too late for the marketplace and all the effort is lost. Every timely step increases the potential for his product. In each step there is a point of no return.

In recent years, a longshoreman's strike made it impossible to unload shipments of Central American bananas at American ports. The banana boats kept their communications open for news that the strike was over until the bananas were near the port. If the answer was "no," there was a point where the bananas were dumped at sea and the boat patiently returned to Central America for another load.

The reason? Bananas start their journey green. Delivery is timed so the banana is near its peak when it reaches the markets. If it remains too long aboard ship, it spoils. It is better to abort and start over repeatedly than to be caught with a boatload of over-ripe fruit.

Much of the chain of food and fiber from the land to the consumer is dependent upon strict timing at many points in order to preserve its potential.

King's and queen's heads have rolled because they ran out of time to produce an heir, which would have added a potential — a continuity — to the reign. An aging king with no heir becomes a lame duck. Those with vested interests in the potential — the continuation of rule — are quick to change allegiance. It is one of the requirements of self-preservation.

The action concerning the banana boat, the kingdom and farming are all defensive measures. Each must, through proper timing, preserve and extend its potential — or it will be superceded by one which is more adept at the game.

Perhaps you have noticed that every phase of life is governed by the observance of these two factors: timing and potential — each leaning upon the other. When you have run out of one, you have exhausted the other. Caution, planning, luck and perhaps many other factors govern timing and potential, but, however it works — timing and potential govern us.

Clearing New Ground

We were a farm family.

We didn't live on a farm at the time. We were inclined that way, but we just couldn't afford the luxury then.

My daddy was doing automobile repairs. He was a specialist at fixin' the rear-ends of Maxwell cars. He later graduated from the broken axle department to become a dealer of those newfangled contraptions from Detroit and elsewhere. But, right then he was complaining about how aggravating it was to re-assemble the hind part of a Maxwell.

I asked him if that was the hardest job in the world (being a small boy, I needed to know these things in order to be able to dodge them when I grew up). He thought a little while and then he answered:

"Not by a long shot."

Naturally, my following question was direct and to the point:

"What is the hardest job in the world?"

Without any further hesitation or beatin' around the bush, he said:

"Clearing new ground."

He didn't mean with a bulldozer or modern earth-moving equipment. He meant with mules, trace chains, hand axes, grubbin' hoes, pull-saws, muscles and sweat.

Daddy said what made it twice as hard was that grandpa, being a God fearin' man, didn't allow no cussin' and he said clearin' new ground by hand, without cussin' was an almost unbearable condition.

He was talking about 60 to 70 years ago, when people didn't buy much fertilizer. When they wore out the land, instead of trying to restore its productivity with guano, they just cleared up some more. He said that was why a lot of young men left the farm. It wasn't to see the bright lights in the city. It was to get away from the new ground department.

I never did ask him but I guess he gave me the reason why he spent many of his younger days under the rear-end of a Maxwell.

Company Store Blues

I n the first 30 or 40 years of this century, there was a lot of sickness, misery and failure among the small farmers of the south. As failure graduated into total ruin, farm families moved to the cotton mills for jobs that paid anywhere from around 50 cents a day to 10 cents an hour.

There was no government aid, no programs or loans for farmers in the early days. If you wrote your congressman, he would send you some literature and a few packages of garden seed.

The following is composed of bits of thought and expression that could be heard from the washed out people who might be anywhere misery found company.

The migration to the mills was thought of as *failure,* and those who went promised themselves that they would return to the farm "just as soon as they were able." Some did. Some didn't.

Their soliloquy went something like this:

Not 'nough of nothin' ... crops have failed again ... Fertilizer man ... says we need a friend.

Grass got the garden ... The cow has gone dry ... Nothin' left to sell ... Not a dime laid by.

Can't kill a rabbit ... Can't find a squirrel ... Nothin' but 'possums ... in the whole darn world.

Makin' fifty cents ... dippin' turpentine ... Get one step ahead ... slip two steps behind.

Back-breakin' ... man-killin' ... gnat-eatin' ... job.

Must be sumpin better ... can't be nothin' worse ...
Shout hallelujah! ... Call the deadman's hearse.

Goin' back to the mills ... we can't do no harm ...
Save up some money ... then back to the farm.

Make ten cents an hour ... ten hours make a buck ...
Beats stayin' on the land ... with our kind o' luck.

Mister freight-train man ... this here ain't no bum ...
Look out company store ... here we come.

The Baying of Hounds

There is a difference in the yapping of city-bred dogs and the late-night baying of farm-raised hounds. The agitation of closely-held dogs serves to break the peace of communities and cause those who seek slumber to curse the insensitivity of their neighbors.

But the hounds that raise their voices to join in a chorus and relay it from farm to farm, do so with a solemn dignity that salutes the night.

It is perhaps true that they "are baying at the moon," but it has seemed to those who have been privileged to hear these base-string notes that the dogs have intended a reassurance to all in their area of care.

There are many who say there is no finer sound than fox dogs in full pursuit while the hunters sit around a fire and identify the voices in the distance. There are others who are moved by the anxious barking at the treeing of a 'possum or a 'coon.

Hunting dogs, pursuing dogs, ferreting dogs, watch dogs — all have their place and their special voices.

But, for reassurance of the peace and tranquility of a countryside, nothing can take the place of the rhythmic baying of farm hounds in the late hours of a quiet night.

6

ESCAPING WEDHOOD

I once had the good fortune to spend an afternoon in the presence of an itenerant sewing machine salesman. He used to travel through the countryside, demonstrating sewing machines ...

Escaping Wedhood

Among the *all kinds of people in the world,* there are the nine-to-five folks and the can-to-cain't folks.

It is generally conceded that there isn't much use for nine-to-five folks to talk to other nine-to-fivers. All know what all the rest know, just like the can-to-cain'ters. If one of either group will talk to the other, they'll likely learn something. If you *ever* see such an interchange, you can bet that information is being passed on.

But, if you want to hear some colorful and tantalizing stories, you've got to converse with a once-in-a-whiler or a seldom-if-ever professional.

I once had the good fortune to spend an afternoon in the presence of an itinerant sewing machine salesman. He used to travel through the countryside, demonstrating sewing machines.

A sewing machine salesman was of a specific type; having his own special tendencies, attributes and style. They are not to be confused with lightnin' rod salesmen, whom they claimed to be a grade above.

Sewing machine men carried a demonstrator

machine along with them, which lent the aura of being among the technical professionals.

The men in the periphery of their audiences entertained some lingering suspicions about their masculinity, because they could sew like women.

It was for these above-mentioned reasons that a sewing machine man had to maintain an outgoing personality by telling a constant stream of stories that could be guaranteed to promote laughter and good humor.

And, because of this trait, people in the back country would walk for miles to attend *a demonstration*. In fact, it was the high point of social life in some areas. People came in their best clothes, bearing covered dishes and other refreshments.

The particular expositor of whom I speak had aged in the service of his profession; his face held the lines of one who had seen his share of the vicissitudes — and had drunk most of them.

He, at the moment, was resting between adventures and was telling of his experiences:

He said, "As was the custom, when a demonstration stretched on 'til suppertime, the host invited me to partake of the evening meal.

"I lingered on one such occasion with a family which had a daughter who had passed into puberty several seasons agone. The girl was not the ugliest example I had ever seen, but, in such company, she could hold her own. When she grinned broadly and looked like she was going to jump straddle of you any minute, her gaze missed you on both sides.

"I tried to be friendly and distant at the same time, but as I was coming up the back steps, she grabbed me in a hold that would, in this day and time, be confused with a sexual harassment.

"As I was trying to extricate myself, her daddy came through the door with a double-barrel shotgun and said, 'So, you are dallying with my daughter? I hope you've set the date; elsewise, the undertaker is going to set one for you'.

"I urgently realized the fullest extent of my situation; there was nothing to do but follow the script, so to speak.

"I put my arms around the girl and said, 'Yes. I have found my ideal and I want to do it right.'

"I shook hands with her father, her four brothers; kissed her mother on both cheeks, and said they should select a preacher while I went home to get my new blue serge suit to get married in. To shore up the validity of the situation, I asked if it would be all right to leave my demonstrator sewing machine until I got back.

"That clinched it. Needless to say, they couldn't believe a fellow would give away a $49 sewing machine to escape wedhood."

Root Doctor

An Herb Doctor is sometimes called a Root Doctor. A Root Doctor who is considered an Herbalist (one who concocts treatments from herbs and roots from the ground) is usually considered to be on the more respectable side of the profession.

Those who make "potions" with items such as bat wings, frog intestines, etc., for the purpose of "casting a spell" or "putting on a hex" are known as Witch Doctors, and generally do not enjoy a place of eminent respectability among the professions.

Those who can make good medicine or bad medicine on order are generally referred to as Root Doctors.

"Love potions" are the main demand of patients who feel insecure in their relationship with the opposite sex. That is to say: "Put a hex on him or her and make them love me."

One fellow asked how much it would cost to make a potion that would guarantee the right results. When the Root Doctor told him $25, he said, "How much would it be just to get her to lean my way a little?"

It is generally considered to be unethical practice for the same Root Doctor to sell two conflicting potions on the same subject. That is, one should not sell a love potion for the same lady to two or more rivals ... at the same time. That would be frowned upon.

This, of course, presents the problem where two or more individual Root Doctors are serving the same territory. Quite often this presents a conflict and sometimes the prices for various services are raised or lowered to suit the competition.

One Root Doctor was asked why he conducted his professional offices in such a temporary, run-down, lean-to building. He replied that he never knew when circumstances might require his hurried change of address.

It is easy to see that one who can make love potions,

or put a whammo hex on someone, might be called on, from time to time, to live dangerously. Many leave their motors running as a precautionary measure.

There was a gentleman who practiced in a southern county. He manufactured his own medicine, ordering the ingredients from a Chicago supply house that specialized in vitamins, laxatives, tonics based in alcohol and other dark and messy ingredients.

Those who were afflicted with "lower back pain" and that "run-down feeling," complicated with diseases secured by various social contacts, made a long line at his back door. They had been admonished to bring their own bottles and be ready to fill those bottles themselves from the master container which would be pointed out to them. A further condition was that the Root Doctor would not handle any money, but the patient would notice a small receptacle wherein one might make a financial donation, the minimum being $3 (at that stage of inflation).

All above mentioned precautionary measures were designed to thwart the enforcement of state and federal medical practice laws.

The doctor flourished for several seasons. He bought an increasingly larger automobile each year. He allowed the dollars to stack up and overflow between trips to his buried tomato cans.

One day, when he was closing up shop and leaving with a basket of burdensome cash, three strangers pushed a gun in his ribs and unburdened him. Just as they were leaving, the doctor said, "Easy come, easy go. I got plenty mo'." The gentlemen returned and made him dig up his deposit-garden and one borrowed his new car.

This turn of events so saddened the doctor he withdrew his professional services from that area.

Those Mustard Seed

Caleb was walking home late in the evening after a hard day. All the way, as he passed neighbors' houses, he smelled fatback frying along with thin-fried lace-edged cornbread, and, over it all, the exquisite odor of mixed turnips and mustard.

It ran through his head that all he needed for a supper of fatback, fried cornbread, turnips and mustard, were the turnips and mustard. The hunger pangs motivated his natural instincts and he wondered who among his neighbors and friends might supply his urgent need. He even stopped and chatted with two or three folks to let drop his love of fatback, fried cornbread, turnips and mustard; to no avail. Either they were insensitive or owned no garden patches.

He remembered he had some pepper sauce to go along with the mustard and turnips. You know, when a hungry man gets something like that on his mind, it's mighty hard to get it off, 'specially when its sumpin t'eat like good fried streak-o-lean fatback, a crackly fried hoecake of cornbread, turnips and mustard mixed in a pot with a little piece of pork floating around in lots of potlikker.

Man, he was hungry.

The last place he passed would be the preacher's house. He had a turnip and mustard patch mighty convenient to the path and just around the bend so nobody could see from the pastorium. He didn't like takin' nothin' like that from nobody's garden — especially the Reverend Pastor of the Free For All Baptist Church.

It bothered Caleb, but not for long.

He looked both ways, leaned over and swept up an armload of the green goodies and kept going.

When he walked in the back door, the first thing Wilma said was, "Where did you get them greens?"

Naturally, Caleb was slightly insulted by the tone of her voice which inferred that he might not have acquired them in an acceptable manner.

His answer: "Where you think I got 'em? I got 'em out of a friend's garden."

With remaining doubts, Wilma's reservations melted as she thought of a supper of fried fatback, thin-fried cornbread, turnips and mustard with a little pepper sauce sprinkled on 'em.

It was a fine supper, after which Caleb and Wilma soon got sleepy and stumbled off to bed.

About 3 o'clock in the morning, Caleb woke up with a heavy stomach and a slightly heavy conscience.

All the week, he had little twinges, especially when Wilma kept on asking him all those foolish questions.

The following Sunday, it was time to go to meeting. Caleb wondered how he would feel, looking down the aisle at the Reverend Pastor, and he wondered if the preacher maybe saw him taking the vegetables.

He decided to keep a straight face and maintain his innocence.

During the sermon, after Caleb's conscience had squirmed a while and the sweat on his brow was about to run down his face, the preacher brought into his sermon the "grain of mustard seed." Caleb had missed the before and the after, but the mention of mustard seed came through strong and clear.

As soon as they had gotten back home, Wilma said: "See there, he knows you stole his mustard and turnips. Elsewise, why you think he said that about them mustard seed?"

Caleb felt bad. Here he was: a good brother in the Church and stealin' mustard and turnips from the preacher. He went two or three more days, examining his conscience to find a loophole. He thought about the Lord's reaction, but he concluded that the Lord didn't have no time to worry about a supper of fatback, cornbread, mustard and turnips in potlikker. It was way over into Thursday 'fore his conscience won and he decided to go and talk with the preacher.

"Pastor, I got to tell you; I stole a mess of mustard and turnips from your garden. I tell you, preacher, I am ashamed, but I was sorely tempted ..."

The preacher smiled and laid his hand on Caleb's shoulder: "That's all right, brother; you're welcome. I know just how much you must love, as I do, a supper of fatback, flat cornbread, mustard and turnips, with a little pickle juice spilled on it."

"But, preacher, what you gonna do about me raidin' your garden?"

"Well, Caleb, if you will help me a little next season, we'll just have to plant a bigger garden for both of us."

From Caleb there came a relieved "Thank the Lord and Amen."

7

MENTAL INDIGESTION

Colors are loud, fashions are shocking and mistakes are glaring. Even the "mildness" is shouted and sold to the blare of bugles and the beating of drums.

Mental Indigestion

Some time ago there was talk about a silent recording being put on all juke boxes for those who might slip a quarter in the slot to have the pacifying pause between the groans, the whines and the jumps.

It was argued that many a bedeviled soul would gladly take his portion of alleged entertainment out in silence.

It was an excellent thought and it is hoped that it will be marketed in a new and expanded model and perhaps sold in the large economy size.

In keeping with the movement, we would like to suggest that television have periods of quiet. We know, of course, that some stations, in early morning hours, show a silent and rigid scene known as a test pattern. This is conducive, but coming as it does at the expectant end of the nervewracking pandemonium and patter, it is ill timed. It could serve a greater purpose if it were sandwiched between, during and often.

Colors are loud, fashions are shocking and mistakes are glaring. Even "mildness" is shouted and sold to the blare of bugles and beating of drums.

Somewhere, in some remote and picturesque mountain village, isolated from civilization's constant grind by the gentle undulation of a hundred hills, there may stand a little clapboard cottage. From the approaching quiet country lane it will present a perfect picture of serenity and peace.

But, a dime will get you a dollar that some little knothead is busily bouncing a ball against those lovely clapboards and worrying the heck out of his mama.

Going Around Again

T here are those who believe that you "only go around once" and that you should do it with gusto — even if you must muster the gusto with the help of the hops.

There are others who believe we may go around more than once. They believe our souls are reincarnated in new bodies with new brains and that we go around again — or many times.

This would present at least one answer to what happens to used souls and why some poor souls appear to be more used than others. One wonders at what point it is determined that a soul has been "totalled" and is taken out of service. Some of those we see going around these days appear to be treating their souls rather badly. But, who are we to judge?

Have you ever heard or said, "Oh! I wish I could start over, knowing what I know now?" (Let us dismiss the subject that likely caused such a thought and go on to other things.)

In parts of the world, certain religions believe that people may not necessarily go around again as people, but may be reincarnated as other animals. They won't step on an ant out of fear that they may be killing some higher life that is coming around again in lower form.

But, such consideration doesn't stop them from cursing one another. Their favorite epithet is "son of a dog," and in more civilized regions they even mention the sex of the dog.

So, if you see someone acting more like a low-life animal than a human, just keep in mind that the poor fellow may be going around again.

On Jumping Up and Down

I had gone through most of a rather long life believing and contending that loud and insistent commands were not necessary.

I believed that quiet and reasonable requests were all that were required to carry on affairs.

Only in recent years have I been disillusioned. I have found that calm, kind, moderate requests are too often ignored by those on whose ears they fall. Such quiet approaches are ignored as carrying no urgency or authority. Reasonableness is understood to be weakness or irresolution.

There is also the likelihood that soft words may be lost in the rapid fire and screaming of some radio or record player.

I should have known about this bit of human behavior by watching the diplomatic give and take of the nations of the world. Even the greatest nations, which can afford the best of diplomats, must enforce their entreaties by the roar of their armaments.

This is a sad commentary, and perhaps it would be better left unsaid, but, the fact is that many times it is necessary to jump up and down, shout and raise hell, to make people understand and do what they should have done in the first place.

A Smattering Age

Have you noticed we live in a time in which most practitioners of fields of music, arts and crafts pursue their calling with only a smattering of knowledge?

Most of the great music, both popular and classic, was written more than a hundred years ago.

Also, if you will check the dates at the bottom of the pages in your hymnals, you will notice that a great majority of the better religious music was written and/or composed a hundred years or more ago. Allow a very few exceptions.

Let's not even mention painting.

Of course, I am not qualified to pass judgment on many of these subjects. But, may I plead in defense that I am one of the great unwashed who is yet able to recognize quality after it is universally acclaimed, and feel, therefore, that I might have the right to claim some felicity in recognizing the opposite.

For instance ... those bits of canvas on which sane and sober people are unable to find the top because the alleged subject was sloshed on with a mop. If that be art, it will be shown only in a room separated from the museum with a partition that posts a genteel apology.

We will go into the crafts — builders, mechanics and repairmen in all trades — gingerly. (I do not want to alienate myself from anyone in whose tender mercies I might find myself in the event I should blow a fuse or a gasket.)

But, these gentlemen of the crafts will be the first to tell you that there is a shortage of competent apprentices in their field.

Nobody seems to be interested in excelling at anything anymore.

That is exactly my point.

If you can drive a nail without disfiguring the lumber beyond the diameter of a yard around, you are a carpenter.

If you can R&R a vehicle, car, truck or tractor — that is, remove and replace parts until you stumble upon the right one — you are a mechanic.

And, on and on.

This is just a smattering, of course, but you get the idea.

You know, you know, you know??

Fey, Fate and Fortune

Occasionally, there comes a person who is *touched* — apparently, by whatever gods may be. These people have an other-worldly air or attitude. In romantic realms they are said to be fey. They are not considered eccentric in the usual sense. It is only that they seem to be exempt from some of the forces of circumstance that govern the norm. They tend to know things, feel things and have an awareness that precedes events.

Almost all of you have had occasions to feel this power — the strange knowledge that affairs are falling in a pattern that cannot be accounted for by the ordinary law of averages; it is as if fate had predetermined the end result with its own principles of cause or will, leaving mere man to thrash about without compensatory result for his efforts. Or, if we are reluctant to ascribe this strange power to some level of the supernatural, wherein we sometimes invent our own gods and require tokens, symbols and emblems — from buckeyes to rabbits' feet — we perceive it to be an erratic force that unpredictably determines events. Then we call it luck, destiny, fate or chance.

(Without examples being given) the reader knows from his own experience of instances of intervention, whether divine or just strange, which set patterns of chance that altered reasonable expectations, and demonstrated a power beyond human comprehension.

And, when it happens, in the absence of acceptable

explanation, someone says it's *fate,* it's *fortune* or *he's fey.*

The Tenders and Menders

H ave you ever noticed that there is one particular kind of person the good Lord sprinkled around in barely adequate proportion? Out of every-so-many people, there is one person who is in charge of the undones and loose-ends.

As you know, the world is full of folks who, just by walking through, can leave everything disheveled, unfastened, wide-open, strewn and disorganized.

There are only a select few who are aware and orderly enough to pick up, turn off, put back, close up and repair the devastation.

We are not speaking of the prophets who can look down the road and see havoc coming like hell after a yearling. We are talking about the quiet ones who know what to do to repair the damage after hell has left havoc in its wake.

Some grandmothers used to serve in this capacity. A few still do. Perhaps you can remember one who carried the keys to places worthy of locks; who knew where to find the linament; who wound the clock; who mended things — including hearts; who knew when birthdays came and could help with babies' coming; who put out the cat; who closed doors, raised windows; who didn't have to ask where things were nor what to do next. They were the first ones called when there was trouble — both great and small.

There are a select few of this kind of person. They can be identified early in life. There is no explanation for them. They are the tenders and the menders of the world and caretakers of the human sheep. They are the responsible ones.

Thank the Lord for the few He has sent and let's all pray that He spare a few more.

Fraught

Occasionally, writers who must produce columns at regular intervals run out of subjects. We find ourselves with nothing to say and several inches of space in which to say it.

Those who exercise proper judgment substitute some other material for which they may escape blame.

Even more often, we have a subject but, after due consideration, we discover that it is too hot to handle. If we pursue it, we usually use up all of our space with disclaimers or expiating explanations.

I have, however, found a long-neglected subject on which little has ever been said:

It is the good word "FRAUGHT."

Everybody knows what that means — or do they?

The first definition is "loaded," as loaded with meaning; fraught with meaning. A boat can be fraughted, that is: loaded. But, the definition that I like is: "A fraught of water requires two buckets." One bucket is not a fraught. Everyone knows that it is easier to carry two buckets than one. One bucket of water is quite inconvenient while two buckets balance the load.

In some countries, water carriers use a pliant stick across their shoulders, which gives a little spring as the carrier walks with a bucket on each end. He is thereby transporting a fraught of water.

Let us then move the word into the realm of reason and suggest that a "subject that is fraught with" whatever potential might be a matter that is balanced with legitimate consideration from two sides or both ends of the stick.

Therefore, "fraught" requires no disclaimers; it admits the existence of a complementing load, be it the same or opposite.

With all the conflicts in the world, in which door slammings, gate closings and bridge burnings constitute a final solution, surely some respect should be given to the good word "fraught," which admits of a coexistence of a counterpart, and from which the world of reason and accommodation may exist in a balance from both ends of the stick.

Rescued Houses

Old houses, standing alone, have an austere dignity and personality of their own. Those having families to protect show an attitude that foretells the gradation of their charges. The self-respecting and the prudent, the relaxed ne'er-do-wells, whichever, could find their attitudes amplified by their dwellings — if they would only look.

Houses may stand with defensive glares, shielding their embarrassment. Others might lower their eyes and seem to whimper.

The broken lines and sagging seams of their architecture are said to result from their age and the weather, but perhaps not; maybe their etched lines of character come, as do those of their occupants, from joy or the pain of life's vicissitudes. A broken gate or sagging roof line didn't just happen; it took more than the wind and the rain.

If there is no debility nor neglect, if there is a pride that meets you halfway down the road, if happiness and friendliness show up in every line, you may anticipate that a prideful and pleasant family will dwell therein.

If the house has been abandoned, you will know it by the indictment of its gaze and the resentment of its isolation. People who pass will say, "I believe that house is empty" and "nobody seems to live there anymore." They will know without being told.

But now, because of the dearness of new construction, many old houses are being rescued. And, when you see one that has been rebuilt, the first thing you will notice is the dignity and graceful pride of the house itself. It is almost as if it were saying "Thank goodness; someone finally noticed."

8

MONEY MATTERS

People have lost confidence in anybody who presumes to discourse on the "economy." In fact, the quickest way to give an audience that "somewhere else" look is to just mention the subject ...

Money Matters

People have lost confidence in anybody who presumes to discourse on the "economy." In fact, the quickest way to give an audience that "somewhere else" look is to just mention the subject.

Of course, it's all right to talk about "money." That's different. Not enough. Too much. When, where, how and where-did-it-go? There used to be other subheads, mainly under the general headings of "getting-along-without" and "making do."

For instance; the life of a pair of pants is now determined by the width of the legs and cuffs or the belt loops. It used to depend on whether or not they still had a seat.

The life of a shirt is now determined by the size and shape of a collar. It used to depend on whether or not a frayed collar could be "turned."

"A good 10 cent handkerchief" now costs at least a dollar.

The life of a tie depends upon its width. It was once determined by the number and the gravity of gravy spots.

You won't believe it, but the 1927 Sears Roebuck catalog offered; all-wool blankets for $6.95 per pair; cotton blankets, $1.72 a pair; men's wool suits from $10 to $27.50; all-wool overcoats — the finest — $12.50; ladies and men's finest dress shoes, $4.40 a pair; ladies dresses, $3.79 to $8.95; foot-powered sewing machine, $33.95; electric model sewing machine, $59.50.

How about men's or women's heavy-ribbed cotton union suits (imagine), 68 cents to $1.50; auto tires, guaranteed 8,000 miles, $5.95 up; auto battery, guaranteed 18 months, $8.95 up; hammerless double-barrel take-down model shotgun, $18.95; solid silver tableware, example six heavy teaspoons, for $8?

People who go around quoting such figures fail to tell you that the regular day's wages at that time was from 50 cents to $1.50. Now, that was per day — usually about 10 hours.

In spite of inflation, high taxes, high energy costs, etc. things are better than they once were.

Fire Sale

How long has it been since you've seen a good old fashioned fire sale?

They used to be fairly regularly scheduled events. There would be a lot of smoke, with very little damage — almost always in a dry goods store. Next morning a large banner would be strung across the front of the store saying "FIRE SALE. Smoke-damaged merchandise at giveaway prices."

When asked about the damage, the clerks would wave toward the back of the store and say something about "just smoke up here."

There must have been some kind of chemical that gave out that burned odor. You could smell it halfway down the street.

Of course, I am sure there were some genuine, unfortunate fires from time to time. But, there were also some staged events for publicity and for attracting buyers who were looking for bargains.

When a "Fire Sale" got to going real good, it became necessary to haul in more merchandise at night to replenish the shelves and counters. It could go on for several months.

It reminded you of the fellow on a country road who dragged stuck cars out of a mud hole for $20 each. He said it was about to kill him, working day and night. When asked if there was that much traffic at night, he said, "No, but at night I have to haul water for the mud hole."

Another merchant might sell a pair of shoes, marked down 35 cents from the original price, and hand the shoes directly to the customer without wrapping. He would wring his hands and say, "Take them. I can't afford to give you the box at that price. Tell your friends."

One merchant claimed he always sold everything below cost. When asked how he made a living doing that, he said he survived by taking the cash discount on the wrapping paper.

In one town where the train tracks came in front of the stores, a merchant arranged for the use of an empty boxcar. He loaded it with overalls, work pants, etc., and put a big sign on the side: "I can't afford to unload them at this price. Buy them here, straight from the factory." People stood in line to buy them at the same price all the other stores were getting.

There were three dry goods stores side by side. The poor fellow in the middle came down one morning to find that the store on the left had a large "Bankrupt Sale" sign. The store on the right was covered with a "Fire Sale" banner.

He rushed down and had a big sign painted and hung across his middle building. It simply said "Main Entrance."

Now you know why so many merchants up at the malls are having to close their doors — it's against house rules to have fire sales.

What do they know about business?

Don't ask!

On Being Rich — Temporarily

I t is the custom for most folks to exist in what is compassionately referred to as austere circumstances.

Such has been our experience — except in one instance.

Sometime ago we received an unaccountable government check for $5,097.96. We knew better than to spend it, but while we were holding it, nervously, another check from the same source arrived in the amount of $11,286.78.

In our heart we knew, but it didn't keep us from hoping that perhaps somewhere, somehow, the government had discovered our plight. Or, that we had inadvertently passed "GO" and had thereby become entitled.

We did not do a stupid thing like returning the checks immediately, but we did write the office concerned and asked them "to what should we credit these payments?"

That seemed subtle enough, and it was.

We got a prompt reply: Return the checks immediately if not before.

Thus ended our sally into the world of the affluent.

Since that time, we have heard of a couple of similar instances.

The first is said to have happened to an official in a computer company (which is an instance of just retribution).

The gentleman borrowed from a bank and duly repaid the loan on time. In a few days he received a collection letter that said he "owed the sum of 0.00 dollars." Of course, he ignored the letter.

A few days later he received a similar letter, more insistent and listing the amount in arrears as "0.00 dollars," again.

Shortly thereafter, a letter arrived, threatening to sue by a certain date if they did not receive a check for "0.00 dollars."

Upon that ultimatum, the poor fellow sat down and wrote the bank a check in full "for the amount of 0.00 dollars." That settled the matter. He has heard no further.

Another instance: An automatic mailing machine for a big mail order company is said to have sent some poor fellow 40,000 catalogs, all at one time.

Litigatin'

T he chief justice of the Supreme Court once cast aspersions on some members of the legal profession. He called attention to the crowded dockets and the crowded jails. He blamed the condition on the lawyers who too often involve themselves in litigation that allegedly borders on the unethical.

Now many lawyers are happy to take cases on *contingency* or *on halves* so to speak, but they do like to have some slight chance of success.

And other times, lawyers take cases because they're appointed by the court to do so. Here's a case in point:

A fellow was being sued in two cases. He could not afford an attorney to defend him in both cases, but he could scrape up a small fee for the first case.

Because of the high cost of defense, he decided deliberately to lose the first case, after which he would be broke and thereby eligible for free legal services in the second case.

He won the second case because of the composition of the jury rather than the merits of the case. But, the results were the same — he was broke — except for the fact that he had become eligible for a very low grade bankruptcy.

He gained very little by attaining this category, but his credit resumed its accustomed rating since he would not again be eligible to file bankruptcy for six years. The six years would free him from being sued or garnisheed.

Used car salesmen and small loan dealers again sought his patronage and he regained his position in the community. He was reinstated on the regular mailings of all the better sucker lists that he had previously enjoyed.

He was heard to say, "There ain't nothing like having the advice of a good lawyer — especially if he is free."

When Whit Blount Turned the Tide

There has grown up a feeling in this country that one person, by himself, can't change anything and that there is no use to try. Because of this, we expect everything to be the result of a general consensus or accomplished only with great power.

Our community once witnessed a case in which an individual citizen was able to reverse policy and action in litigation by the Federal anti-trust department.

The late C. Whit Blount was owner and operator of the Waynesboro Groceteria, had served as president of the local Rotary Club and was one of the community's business and civic leaders.

At that time, almost 35 years ago, he published an advertisement in defense of his leading competitor, the A&P Tea Company, which was being sued by the Federal Government.

The fine sportsmanship shown by this gesture was recognized by an editorial published in *The Atlanta Journal.* That article, quoting the advertisement, is given below:

COMPETITOR DENOUNCES SUIT AGAINST A&P

A bold three-column advertisement in The True Citizen *catches the reader's eye. We quote it in full:*

A WORD FOR OUR COMPETITOR

There has been a move by the Anti-trust department of the Federal government to destroy our leading competitor, The A&P Food Store.

It may seem odd, but we are opposed to this move.

The A&P Company is definitely our strongest competitor. They keep us hopping. But, we are still in business — and expanding. We do it by selling quality merchandise, buying at a close margin and selling at a closer margin.

The so-called "trust-busters" charge that the A&P Company controls some of the production and processing ends of the food business. As a result, they hold their cost prices down on foods.

WELL, WHAT'S WRONG WITH THIS?

If A&P holds the costs down, it makes our suppliers hold their costs down to the same competitive level. They can sell cheaper, AND SO CAN WE.

We intend to continue to try to sell better merchan-

dise than A&P. We also will continue to have competitive prices.

BUT, we don't believe the government, or any individual, should try to break up a firm that is doing a good, clean, efficient job of serving the people of this country.

(Signed) C. Whit Blount

The Journal's editorial department wrote:

To our notion that advertisement by C. Whit Blount states the economics and the governmental aspects of the suit against A&P with a clarity and a forcefulness that most of the editorial comment has lacked.

Also, it strikes us as a fine example of sportsmanship in business.

Incidentally, it is about as effective an advertisement as could have been written for Mr. Blount's Groceteria.

Makes you sort of wish you were in Waynesboro to trade with him, doesn't it?

In addition to the recognition given by the Journal, The A&P Tea Company picked up the advertisement and the Journal editorial and spent several hundred thousand dollars publishing them in more than 2,000 newspapers in 39 states.

In a few days, Whit Blount was deluged with personal letters from people all over the country. Presidents of the largest business and civic organizations took time to thank him.

In a few weeks, the Federal Trust Department dropped the suit against A&P.

A small merchant in a little town had turned the tide and changed the policy of a department of the biggest government in the world.

Insurance Claim

An insurance agent handed me the following story. It's an old story, but it's possible there is a need to know such matters.

The following was part of a "report of how an accident happened" in a claim for insurance:

The Case of the Busted Brick Barrel

"When I got to the building, I found that the storm had knocked some bricks off the top. So, I rigged up a beam, with a pulley at the top of the building. I then hoisted up a couple of barrels full of bricks. When I had repaired the building, there were a lot of bricks left over so I filled a barrel with those extra bricks. Next, I went to the bottom of the building and untied the line that went through the pulley at the top of the building.

"Unfortunately, the barrel of bricks was heavier than I am. Before I knew what was happening, the barrel started down, jerking me off the ground. I decided to hang on. Halfway up, I met the barrel coming down, and the result was that I received a severe blow on the shoulder. I continued to the top of the building, where I banged my head against the beam, and jammed my finger on the edges.

"When the barrel hit the ground, it burst its bottom. This allowed all the bricks to spill out. I now was heavier than the barrel, so I started down at high speed. Halfway down, I met the barrel coming up, and severely injured my shin. When I hit the bottom I landed on the bricks and got several painful cuts from the sharp edges.

"At this point I must have lost my presence of mind. I let go of the line. The barrel came down and gave me another heavy blow on the head. This put me in the hospital.

"I'm happy to say, however, that I recovered from this most unfortunate incident, and my hospitalization policy paid for darn near everything except the barrel. But it wasn't worth much anyhow."

9

SUNDAY BLUES

What did people do on Sundays before radio, TV and wall-to-wall autos? If you happened to be a newspaper delivery boy almost 60 years ago, you would remember ...

Sunday Blues

W hat did people do on Sundays before radio, TV and wall-to-wall autos?

If you happened to be a newspaper delivery boy almost 60 years ago, you would remember:

The men living on some streets would loll around on their porches in their undershirts and pants, barefooted and unshaven, while the women cooked Sunday dinner.

In some sections of town, big-mouthed women displayed their ignorance by fussing at their husbands and children in a loud voice, so their neighbors a block away were well acquainted with their domestic relations.

Sometimes a neighborhood had a "shade tree" barber and all the men got their hair skint-cut on Sunday evenings.

Girls and young women curled one another's hair. On one side of town folks would be trying to put a curl in their hair while, on the other, folks would be trying to straighten their's.

Most communities had a stand where some of the men went for a shoeshine and to pick up a Sunday paper. Each cost a dime and occasionally a big spender would tip 5 or 10 cents.

Of course, church-going folks got busy early Sunday morning, getting dressed. In summertime it was an excruciating undertaking. Shirt collars had to be buttoned up and little boys had to wedge their feet into too-tight shoes. By the time they were ready for church, red-faced and uptight mamas were in no mood to benefit from the blessings of the occasion. Many a little knothead had his face slapped just before he learned about turning the other cheek.

Some families walked to church. In such cases, many of the men arranged to have a cigar to smoke on the way, which they felt added dignity to the occasion. Usually the cigars were "two-fers" which meant they were two for a nickel. Those who could finance one would smoke a 10-cent "Corona Corona" and they would preserve the distinctive gold band until the stub got so short that it would endanger the upper lip.

Whatever people do now on Sundays, they don't do it on the front porch as they did 60 years ago. Perhaps the reason is that they can't hook up the TV, VCR, radio and tape player on the porch. Whatever activities they carry on are done inside the house where the screaming and hollering can have a proper musical background and blend with the family confusion.

Many people used to live in long, narrow houses that took up about half the lot from front to back. They were called "shotgun" houses because you could look in the front door and see the back door. The other half of the lot held the vegetable garden, including two rows of collards.

Now, people have turned the house sideways on the

lot and call it ranch style. They've screened the porch and call it a breezeway. They've poured a concrete slab at the back door and refer to it as the patio.

The resident honcho used to sit on the front porch on Sunday evenings, wearing his undershirt and sipping his homebrew.

Now, he sits on the patio, wearing an imprinted T-shirt, drinking store-bought beer.

Things certainly have changed — or have they?

Country Commissary

T
he pattern of retail merchandising has changed over the years. There is very little retail credit on groceries and small things. People pay cash for these and use their credit for larger and more expensive items.

Very few people now remember The Country Commissary, The Country Store and The Company Store. All were alike but different. Each got a bad name for abusing its customers. Sometimes the stores were falsely accused, for they were often the last best hope of the people they served.

The Country Store might be a crossroads building stocked with almost every kind of merchandise, sold principally for cash, but a few short-term "tickets" might have been kept on the side.

The Country Commissary was generally dominated by trade from one big farm or a small group of farms which "stood good" for their tenants or sharecroppers.

The credit arrangements were not short-term; they were from harvest-to-harvest or from year-to-year.

Quite often the line of credit was spelled out: So many gallons of syrup, pounds of fatback, bushels of meal, sacks of salt, lard, flour, medicine, snuff, tobacco, pairs of overalls, etc. The items would be released by the week or month.

The tenant tried to supplement this store allowance with a vegetable garden, by raising a hog or two and by keeping a cow. Occasionally, he or his wife might pick up a little "day labor" for cash, at the rate of 50 cents or a dollar a day. Sometimes the extra work was "takin' in washin', etc."

The farm commissary might keep a "complete line" for other customers, but served mainly as a dispensary of the staple items, which were often homemade on the farm. Sometimes the store was open only on Saturdays.

Those who saw only abuse in the system pointed out that the laborer or tenant was charged more than the cash customer. This was true, but it is still true; credit costs considerably more than cash, whether it is through bank credit or easy terms.

Usually, the commissary customer could not have gotten credit anywhere else. His arrangement with the commissary was his financial salvation.

There were sometimes abuses by the operators, but often there were abuses by those who received the credit. If a tenant family found the situation too intolerable, it might take a moonlight walk to other territory.

The Farm Commissary, which also had related enterprises that required the paying of daily or weekly wages, might pay off in "script" or metal tokens that could only be spent at the commissary. Of course, this lent itself to abuse by monopolizing the flow of trade. Again, however, this was not always by design. Quite often the practice helped to make possible trade, jobs and local enterprise that otherwise could not have contributed to the local economy.

Company Stores were usually located in manufacturing, sawmill or cotton mill towns. The workers usually traded at The Company Store because it was the only place they could get credit. Prices were usually higher at these credit sources, but the cost of extending credit, keeping books and doing business added to the burden.

The flimsy nature of the economy and the burden the working man carried in those days created the commissary system and usually received the brunt of his discontent. A great many people lived in a state of financial misery that would be difficult to understand now. They needed a focus for this discontent. It usually turned to The Country Commissary or The Company Store.

The Circus Parade

You don't see them much anymore; circus parades, I mean.

You remember how the steam calliope could be heard for miles? Older children used to run alongside and watch the man playing.

The circus used to look big, vigorous and imposing.

People lined the sidewalks on the parade route. Mamas and daddies looked to the safety of the children when the tigers, lions and elephants came by.

Most of the elephants would walk single-file — one behind the other; each holding onto the tail of the one in front.

One time in our town, a rich fellow in a big Packard got in a hurry while waiting for the string of elephants to get out of his way. His foot slipped off the brake pedal and his big Packard slammed into the last elephant in line. It caused quite a commotion.

The circus manager came running up, wringing his hands and hollering.

The fellow in the Packard said, "Don't worry, I can afford to pay for one elephant."

The circus man screamed, "One elephant, what do you mean ONE elephant? Why, fellow, you know how elephants walk, each holding onto the tail of the one in front? Mister, you have just snatched the rear-end out of 10 elephants."

What Do You Always Say?

One thing about TV: it has brought into the house what somebody used to have to go and get over the back fence — if you remember, 'frinstance:

Well, Maddie Jane, has Saddie Sue been by to see you yet? Looks like she would, seein' as how she and your Bennie used to be so close. She's been gone from here nearly three years. You ought to remember; she left on the midnight train just a few days after your Bennie ran away and joined the army ... some people tried to read something into it ... both of them leavin' town suddenly and so close together ... well, of course, I never put no store in gossip like that ... like I told all my neighbors; what if they did? They wouldn't a been the first ones ... why, I remember ... uh, well.

What I wanted to say was: Saddie Sue come by to see me yesterday ... Saw her coming down the road in that big Studebaker with the window glasses all around ... she and her boyfriend, that Mr. Renaldo, settin' in the back seat while their pistol totin' chauffeur is drivin'. They park out front and the men stay in the car while Saddie Sue prances in wearin' her new, store-bought clothes. She hugs me and I ask if the menfolks won't come in. She says no thanks, that Mr. Renaldo rather set out in the car where his cigar won't bother anybody.

I says, baby, what you been doin' and where have you been doin' it? ... she says, well, I been workin' in a variety store up in Chattanooga until recently ... I says, shorely you didn't get them pretty clothes out of no variety store ... she says, no, Mr. Renaldo bought them for me.

I says, honey, who is this Mr. Renaldo and what's he do for a livin'? ... she says, he don't say, but when I mention it, he just says, "I got connections in New York and Chicago." I don't know what he means by connections, but they must pay pretty good.

I says, Saddie Sue, how did you meet Mr. Renaldo? She says, well, you know, I feel so honored. He came in the house and walked past all the other girls and came back to the bar and says "I choose you." I mean, in the variety store, you know ... well, with his money and connections, he could have had anyone he wanted, and he chose me. Ain't I lucky? I says, shore looks like it, honey: If you've made connections with a man who has connections, sounds to me like you have done the best you can with the talents you've got — like the good book says.

That's what I always say ... what do you always say, Maddie Jane?

Job's Turkey

There have been some ups and downs recently in the economy.

Fortunately, most people who talk about poverty today don't have the slightest idea of what they are talking about. It is seldom that circumstances of deprivation equal those of the Great Depression.

There used to be an expression: "As poor as Job's turkey."

I never knew what that meant, but I've seen the time that I thought Job was very well off if he had a turkey, regardless of the financial condition of the turkey.

In the depression, people used to tell stories about their poverty to make themselves laugh to keep from crying.

I remember a few of them:

One fellow said his pants were worn so thin in the seat that you could read the print on his flour-sack shorts through them well enough to determine whether the flour was self-rising or plain.

A group of families owned a 15 cent soup bone. It was borrowed around the neighborhood to make soup on until it was finally worn out.

Another story similar to the first was that a fellow's shoe soles were so thin that he could stop on a dime and tell whether it was heads or tails.

A farmer had a mule that was starving. He swapped the mule for a load of hay. It was then he realized that he had no mule to eat the hay. But, the man he traded with was a nice fellow and loaned him the mule until it could eat up the hay.

One poor fellow fell under a steam roller. He didn't have time to get out, but in order to preserve the best from the situation, he flipped over on his side to keep the crease in his pants.

Another fellow dropped his last dime through a crack in the floor. He couldn't justify tearing up the floor to recover the dime. So, he borrowed a $20 bill and pushed it through the crack so it would be worthwhile to tear up the floor.

Back then, if disaster hit a fellow, everybody else welcomed him to the club.

Seriously, during the Great Depression, the little animals — squirrels, 'coons, 'possums, rabbits, etc. — were almost hunted to extinction. Game meat was the only meat some folks had. They couldn't afford 5-cent-a-pound fatback or 15-cent-a-pound steak.

As I've mentioned before, in the midst of the depression many people wrote their congressman for help. The government thought it ought to do something. There was a provision made to answer requests for help by sending out five small packages of vegetable seed with instructions on the best way to plant a garden.

10

SPECKS IN THE GRITS

The sheriff said, " ... I am sure that 99 percent of the time those little dark things are okay. But then, on the other hand ... I am going to continue to worry about that other one percent ..."

Cousin Carrie the Executive

Everybody in the settlement knew Cousin Carrie and her sorry husband, Dave. Well, Dave wasn't exactly sorry; he wasn't bad, but he was not one to try to amount to anything.

They lived on 40 acres of bottom land that Cousin Carrie had inherited. They made a living on it. He farmed 39 acres and made enough corn to swap it to a friendly stiller who paid him with a year's supply of medium grade corn liquor.

Carrie, with her vegetable garden, cow, chickens, pigs and fruit trees, made them a living on the one other acre.

They had grown old believing that they were living the average, normal existence. Then came the paving of the big road by their house, bringing the Yankee tourists and the flat-landers. People were always stopping by the house, taking pictures and saying that word "Quaint." They all seemed to want to buy something. Carrie took to selling them jars of her pear preserves.

It was while she was making labels with a crayon that the idea came to her: why not make up several big batches, put them in pint and half-pint Mason jars with the screw-on caps, have her some labels printed and cater to the front yard trade?

Her recipe was very much like all others, but a secret ingredient crept in that altered her entire future — when the preserves were put in the jars to cool before sealing with the metal screw-on tops, Dave went in the kitchen while Carrie was catching her breath on the front porch and poured him a drink from his stashed store. While doing so, he sloshed a little in several of the cooling jars. Only a few drops in each container altered the recipe.

To shorten a long story: all customers became repeat customers. In fact, people on long trips would turn around and come back for more preserves. People begged for a list of the ingredients. Dave had to tell Carrie about his contribution to the concoction and Carrie made it part of the recipe.

In a very short time, "Cousin Carrie's Pear Preserves" were in popular demand. The cooking was being done in vats; pears were being bought from the entire section of the mountains; Ball Mason jars were being hauled in by the van load; Cousin Carrie had her picture on the labels dressed in her apron and mountain-woman bonnet; she required the help of an attorney and a full-time bookkeeper and tax man.

Cousin Dave contributed his share — it took so much of his corn crop to make the few-drops-per-jar special ingredient, that there were times he didn't have a drop left to drink.

Ambulance Spelled Backward

H edgerow didn't have an ambulance.
Rural Huggins, cousin to Sheriff Elbert Huggins, was a public spirited young fellow who liked to be prominent in matters of an important nature (some said hyperactive). He owned an old delivery van which he converted into a make-do ambulance. He equipped it with a blinking light and a stuttering siren. If business was slow he would ride around the community while blowing the siren just to try to stir up activity.

It was while cruising thusly that he came upon an accident of a fellow on a motorcycle. You remember, it was that fellow riding with his Naugahyde jacket on backward who had pitched over in a sandbed. Rural, seeing the backward jacket, thought the fellow's neck had got twisted. He tried to turn it around right; like to have killed him.

Well, the rider didn't appreciate the good efforts of the amateur ambulance driver. He threatened to sue Rural and rushed home to tell his daddy about it just as soon as his neck settled down to normal. It happened his dad manufactured real ambulances, and he was irate at the kind of vehicle his son had been forced to ride in.

Rural didn't perceive the kind of trouble that might come. He went right on with his pseudo-normal activities.

Sometimes he would get a maternity case when the paternity end of the deal happened to be out of pocket at the time the blessed event threatened. When his timing was sometimes bad, he had to remind his customer he was doing it for free — anyway.

In the meantime, the one gnawing ambition of Rural and his associates was to have ambulance spelled backward across the front of his vehicle, like the fellows in the big towns.

Eustice Whitlock, who had painted most of the misspelled signs in the neighborhood, had been commissioned to paint the reverse AMBULANCE for Rural. He was waiting until he could figure out how to paint a word so that the only way it would look right was through a rearview mirror.

Rural finally proposed the solution: He said, "Eustice, it is a fairly simple thing. All you have got to do is paint over your shoulder while holding a hand-mirror in front of you."

Eustice acknowledged that this must indeed be the solution, and he ought to have thought of it himself.

After spilling paint all over himself and the mirror and ruining two pairs of overalls, the sign looked like this:

Straight in: ECNALUBMA and like this through a rearview mirror: ƎƆИA⅃U乗MA.

Strangers, seeing the sign through their rearview mirrors, while hearing the stuttering siren and seeing the blinking light, would often take off across a plowed field. Women would sometimes jam on the brakes, throw up their hands and scream, "The Russians are coming."

There is no telling how things would have finally come out, but the motorcycle rider brought his daddy, the ambulance manufacturer, down to see who they were going to sue for damages.

After looking the situation over, the daddy decided not to sue. In fact, he decided that Hedgerow would be a good place to donate one of his products.

Ambulance was spelled backward at the factory.

Specks in the Grits

One morning, I was sitting down at the Greasy Spoon, watching Sheriff Elbert Huggins while he ate his breakfast. He had just come in from an all-night still-watchin' party and I didn't expect him to have his mind on much of anything. I was therefore somewhat surprised that he was in the mood to discourse on topics of a learned nature.

He was busy picking the specks out of his grits, when he said that he was reminded of some of the great salesmen he had known.

He said, "You know, most people didn't used to like specks in their grits. They thought of all the things those little specks might be; like ground up corn weevils, etc. and the like.

"Well," he went on to say, "Mr. Cason Callaway, who founded Callaway Gardens and a lot of other good things over in west Georgia, also sold grits. He noticed that people didn't especially trust specks in their grits ... after investigating, Mr. Callaway determined that 99 percent of the specks were nothing but part of the corn."

Being the super-salesman he was, he named his grits "The Famous Speckled-Heart Grits." He raised the price a little and, as a result, people came from all over the world, even from Georgia and Alabama, to pay a premium for his grits.

I said, "Well, Sheriff, what do you think about his grits?"

The Sheriff answered with the degree of erudition I had expected. He answered, "I respect the memory of Mr. Callaway. I even buy his grits sometimes. And, I am sure that 99 percent of those little dark things are OK. But, then, on the other hand, if you don't mind, I am going to continue to worry about that other one percent. And, when nobody's looking, I'm going to ease the bigger ones over to one side."

Flamus, Dan and the Klan

Flamus was his name; just Flamus. He stood every day at the same place on the sidewalk, with his back to the wall. Erect; not leaning; ever-alert but unmoving. His eyes roved without the help of his head.

Most people just walked by him as they did any other community fixture, but those who looked him in the face and deliberately spoke were rewarded, as it were, with a smile somewhere between a brick fence and the Mona Lisa.

If asked a direct question, he looked directly at the questioner with a gaze that did not rest easily — it was brought to bear for a short second, accompanied by a blink of the eyes and a slight shrug only of his wrist. He immediately resumed his original position and focused his eyes back on some object on the horizon. This was a complete interview.

When the one who had interrupted had left the area, Flamus' eyes resumed their roving. His silent command seemed to include all he surveyed.

His only contact was a distant friendship for the little boys of the community, who drifted by from time to time and passed a few words.

There was a story, which, of course, was not true, that a nearsighted stranger in town, seeing but dimly the form of Flamus, unmoving, had stepped up on his shoes, stuck a penny in his mouth and looked up into his face to see how much he weighed.

That story is not worthy to be mentioned. Flamus was not mentally deficient; he only pursued his activities with a different approach.

He did not feel any compulsion to comment or render opinions, and, as a result, he did not find it necessary to apologize for anything he had said. Furthermore, he did not feel required to listen to others who felt compelled to run their mouths.

No bully ever challenged him; they did not want to see what he could be capable of with his 6 foot 4 inch, 250 pound, all-muscle body. Sometimes there was conversation about the matter, but it remained at a safe distance.

The only form of life Flamus demonstrated any affection for was Dan, the ice wagon horse. Every day as the wagon made its rounds and stopped at every business and home to dispense ice, Flamus walked away from his post and stood beside Dan, fed him sugar or an apple and stroked his shoulder.

Dan was as stolid as Flamus. He showed no recognition other than to accept the tasty morsel. If Flamus happened to be slow to arrive, Dan would glance fleetingly toward him. Thus, over the years, a friendship grew.

The black citizens and the white citizens of the community enjoyed a peaceful accommodation in the little town and the only excitement was an occasional outburst at the loafers' bench concerning race, or a quiet rumble down near the mullet barrel. It was always understood that neither would be allowed to go any further and that all things were forgotten on the way home.

This understanding quiet was broken when it was discovered that someone had established a local klavern of the klan. Most whites and blacks wondered why. Opposition was about equal. Some said it was because of some riots in the northern cities. Others said it was so the members could have something secret to belong to, and to be able to get away from home.

Nobody was greatly upset until the rumor got out that the Klan was going to have an after-dark parade in their sheets. It was feared that some boisterous citizen might inappropriately bring things to a boil which would lead to injury or mistreatment of innocent parties.

A spokesman for the klan said they had no intention to injure anyone; they just wanted to parade in their sheets. It seemed to be simple enough, and since several fairly level-headed citizens were members, plans proceeded.

Some member, who was a friend of the black iceman, thought it would add dignity to the occasion, to ride old Dan, the icehorse, at the head of the parade. He borrowed the horse for the honor and led out as the sheet-clad members walked behind.

Everything went fine until Dan arrived at his first customer. There he stopped without being asked. That delayed the parade until Dan had waited long enough for a piece of ice to be cut and delivered.

The first two or three stops were slightly embarrassing, but the parade gradually got to the residential section.

In the meantime, little boys, both black and white, hurried by the free-standing Flamus who seemed to be giving them orders out of the corner of his mouth. They hurried away to do his bidding.

In the residential section, Dan was helped with his decisions to stop by small voices from the shrubbery: "Whoa, Dan" and Dan whoaed time after time. The paraders got aggravated at first, later it came to be just as funny to them as to their audience, both black and white, on each side of the streets. Finally, they tired of being a sideshow and quietly broke ranks and carried their sheets home.

Next day the whole town laughed at the incident. That is, everybody but Flamus, who was standing in his usual place, with a ghost of a smile occasionally flickering on his face.

11

SWAPPIN' NICKELS

I don't know exactly the age it starts, but somewhere along the line of least resistance, you come to an awareness that changes your accustomed conduct; you quit spinning your wheels at every new proposal or project; you slow down and wonder ...

Swappin' Nickels

I don't know exactly the age it starts, but somewhere along the line of least resistance, you come to an awareness that changes your course of accustomed conduct; you quit spinning your wheels at every new proposal or project; you slow down and wonder ...

If all new acquaintances are worthy of further cultivation ...

If bigger is automatically better ...

If all business expansion is beneficial to the community ...

If some dollars are worth making ...

If all battles must necessarily be won. (Isn't it better to lose, sometimes?)

This is not some philosophy that espouses defeatism. It is just an attempt to weigh the effort against the lasting results.

We spend a lot of our early years trying to win friends and influence people, many of whom we devote later years trying to insulate ourselves from.

In the early years we acquire homes so large they come to own us and enslave us. Our cars lose their status value and become gas hogs.

As progressive citizens, we want our communities to grow, to get more population, without being aware that, as cities grow, so grow their problems. Merchants contribute their time and money and watch their efforts bring in competition that might put them out of business.

We start noticing a lot of business activity results in swappin' nickels. We believe that we business people must grow or die. Then comes a day when you wonder if this is necessarily so. Where is the point that you stop the frenzy and try to enjoy a pleasant and happy equilibrium?

One of the things that surprises you is the day — in the middle of some public debate or some local or national friction — you suddenly have the feeling you used to have at the picture show, that "this is where I came in."

You realize that all this has happened before; all those things have been said before; many of the panaceas have been tried before and all those crazy people who are presently jumping up and down and screaming are a carbon copy of a hundred crowds ago.

Audacity and Ignorance

Have you noticed that there is a rule-of-thumb belief that general intelligence and the ability to make money do not necessarily go together?

You have seen people who didn't have sense enough to come in out of the rain, but seemed to make money with everything they touched.

One well might conclude that many who have amassed great real estate fortunes since World War II were at least careless. Not always, but often.

You may know of people who were sober investors; who followed all the rules and accumulated nice little nest eggs, only to see their worth destroyed by inflation.

Thirty-five or 40 years ago, insurance companies advertised that you could buy a retirement fund which would guarantee that you and your spouse could retire to luxury in Florida on an income of $200 or $300 a month.

We all know of land that we might have bought for a pittance which now has condominiums shoulder-to-shoulder and is worth midas-millions.

On the other hand, you know of highly intelligent people who aren't able to handle their ordinary affairs, much less manage any money-making enterprise.

I have heard a young man say that he could have made a million dollars from his father's or grandfather's business mistakes. The young man perhaps doesn't know it yet, but, with hindsight, almost anyone could do the same.

Sometimes nothing seems to work.

Once upon a time, members of a family decided, in their early days, to live frugally, invest carefully and build a fortune. They budgeted, lived carefully, omitted many luxuries, invested in safe, sure but slow-growth bonds. They were unostentatious, quiet people who did not seek status. Slowly but surely, their fortune grew to $100,000, $200,000, half a million. Finally, the years and a certain amount of inflation made them millionaires.

By the time they had the million, their habits of economy became so ingrained that they could not bring themselves to enjoy squandering it on extravagant consumption.

They held on; they enjoyed knowing it was there. But, then came the recession. Their millions shrank to almost nothing again.

As their wealth had increased, their neighbors had attributed it to stinginess and plain luck. When it had evaporated, the same people attributed its loss to extravagance and stupidity.

It is believed by some economists that the two greatest contributors to amassing wealth are audacity and ignorance.

Could Mama Stay Home?

Most people do what they believe at the time to be best for their families.

In recent years it has become necessary for both the father and the mother of many families to hold jobs; to bring in two paychecks. Where young children are involved, both parents being away from home has usually required costs for daycare or kindergarten services, plus another auto, plus extra costs for fast-food meals, plus, plus, plus.

There was one fellow whose wife was working. He figured up the total costs of her being away from home and the difference in the income-tax bracket; the amount left over was $3.50 a week. The family was $3.50 better off at the end of the week, after delivering and picking up children; of being exhausted to the point the children got short shrift during the little time available to them. He, therefore, asked his wife to resign her job and again resume her fulltime home-making duties.

Of course, many young households could not cope with modern economics without two incomes. Under such circumstances no one can deny their need. Sometimes, there also is the desire of the young mother not to be "tied down all day with the kids." That is another story, an entirely different story, and one in which the family often gets the little end of the stick.

Although the mental health of married women improves when they are employed outside the home, their husbands seem to suffer psychologically from the change. According to a study at the University of Michigan's Institute for Social Research, such men suffer from severe depression and low self-esteem. The difficulty is that some men's deep-seated family values suffer when their wives begin to work.

Most young (and old) families are now totally dependent on two paychecks. If they stop, every facet and service of the family stops. Those payments and mortgages don't stop.

But, wouldn't it be interesting to know in how many instances things might be better if some families lived in more self-sufficient households; how many would be better off with fewer of their imagined needs; with homegrown, home-prepared, home repaired, less extravagant lifestyles?

And, whether or not the divorce rate might drop?

The Art of Snobbery

There is art in snobbery, but it doesn't require a great deal of intellectual advancement.

Subjects for snobbery vary from the side of town you originate, to whether or not the affluent has old money or new money.

Old money means inherited money. Those who have it, got it whether they would have had sense enough to earn it or not. They got it because one of their ancestors, up the line, acquired it by stooping to some common involvement like working or cheating or just by being there first.

Some of those who inherit old money handle it well while others toss it away, thereby causing their children or grandchildren to have to go to work and acquire some new money, which they would no doubt frown upon.

Then, there are the folks who greet their neighbors' signs of success by jeering their status symbols with, "Look at 'em! Just look at 'em. I knew them when they didn't have a pot to cook in."

Or, if an odious comparison rears its head, you would hear some heated phrases like, "We're just as good as or better than."

There was a time when it was not only important to have money, it was important how the money was made. Up until a fellow got real rich, it was highly preferable that he make it in one of the professions or through speculation or investments.

Money made by a tradesman or craftsman was somehow looked down upon until he got real rich. After that, he took on a higher degree of respectability — even if he made it selling patent medicine or soap or 'shine liquor.

In more recent years, it has not seemed to matter how you got it, but how much you got.

Status symbols are the adult toys with which people astound their neighbors.

Once upon a time, a fellow demonstrated his wealth by using more horses than were actually needed to pull his carriage. If one horse could do the job, he would use two or four.

Later, when automobiles came along, a 35-horse motor might suffice, but people kept surpassing one another until some cars were using 400-horse motors. It took a worldwide fuel shortage to reverse the trend.

Snob appeal runs more to price than quality. Sometimes a high price bespeaks quality, but more often it paves the way for a better bargain sale in the basement.

Labels in ladies' coats are for displaying over the arm or the backs of chairs.

Exclusive place names are for dropping. And old money, who would be quick to deny such practice, would not hesitate to talk of a season near London while shaking a sleeve of English tweed.

Everybody, from those who wear designer jeans with the label across their behinds, to the country clubber with his little alligator on his shirt, indulges in the game.

It's known as genteel snobbery that shouts that "I am just as good as or better than".

Tossin' it Around

Being rich means different things to different people.

I heard one man say that being rich was leaning back against a pretty girl while riding down the road in a limousine and having her peel a grape for you.

For my first several years, my conception of being rich was to be able to buy two 5-cent ice cream cones at one time.

Times were tight when one could afford but one, and even this must be shared with little brother, because of unselfishness and the fact that this good quality was goaded on by urgent parental admonition.

My religious education and my financial struggles admixed somewhat. My parents sent my brothers and me to Sunday School and church, each with a quarter in our hot little hands. The budget was simple — 5 cents for Sunday School, 5 cents for church, 10 cents for the picture show and 5 cents for an ice cream. The pattern was followed strictly, until that day when temptation reared its ugly head. It seemed to us that the great big church was rich enough that it would not miss so small a thing as the 5 cents that was supposed to be dropped in the offering plate. The Sunday School nickel was ajudged to be enough. The juggling of the budget would permit us to buy two ice cream cones or one ice cream cone and a package of popcorn. In any case, the church was not coming out very well in the deal.

I don't recall how many Sundays we operated under the amended budget, but at last came the day: little brother's big mouth spilled the beans.

Our parents lined us up for further instructions. We left with a positive thinking, finger-shaking understanding about the matter and the budget was resumed in its original form.

I am advised by my pastor that churches sometimes still get the small end of the stick when family budgets are set up.

Perhaps we may be forgiven, however, if we remember the day when buying two 5-cent ice cream cones at one time was really tossin' it around.

12

DON'T GET CAUGHT THINKING

Have you ever noticed that we have a peculiar society in its attitude toward mental endeavor?

Trouble Takes a Holiday

It is seldom, but there are occasions when things "go right" . . . times that hold no grief ... when you suddenly realize that no one in your purview is in current conflict ... that your conscience nor your attitude has been altered for several minutes — or even hours.

Such was the case recently.

My horoscope in the morning's paper had said I would "come into some money." Therefore, when I later found a dollar bill in the grass, it was not altogether unexpected.

Considering the nature of the horoscope's promise, I did spend several minutes looking around for money of a higher denomination. Failing in this pursuit, I turned my attention toward other fields. I asked around for trouble, as it were, but found none worthy of attention.

The acting head of the local chapter of "Concerned Citizens" happened by. I asked him how things were going, assuming that if there were any trouble in the community he would be in full charge. He had a paper in his hand, but it was blank. He said that they had no current disaster impending, but he was collecting anticipatory signatures in order to have the jump on the next public project.

It was unnerving to note that he smiled openly as he left.

It would have been a good day for a little trouble, but it seems that fate has no disposition to even out the distribution of untoward events. Bad still comes in bunches. Misfortune too often caters to the same customers.

But, occasionally, a good day comes along, so let's make a mark on the wall.

It is not Always True

I t is said beauty is only skin deep.

That is not always true.

Sometimes beauty settles on a person like a mantle; sometimes it comes from within and carries its own glow.

Haven't you watched the beauty on a mother's face as she returned her new baby's smile?

Have you seen the gentle beauty in the wrinkled face of a grandmother, resting at the end of the day?

Many people's faces are transformed with lines of beauty as they listen to good music.

There are those who look their best in repose, when they are not conscious of being seen.

The beauty of character that denotes love of the land is most evident when a farmer is watching the turning plow. A craftsman's face is chiseled in classic lines as he runs his hands over a job well done.

Have you watched the beauty of anticipation of those who first see home after a long absence?

Have you seen the beauty that comes from satisfaction on the face of a good teacher when a late-blooming student finally begins to unfold?

Wouldn't you like to have seen Christ's face as He delivered the Sermon on the Mount, even more the reflection in the faces of His congregation?

Some beauty is soul-deep.

Don't Get Caught Thinking

Have you noticed that we have a peculiar society in its attitude toward mental endeavor?

It is very acceptable for a person to flaunt his or her physical abilities or endowments. He may talk for hours, with his face jammed full of microphones, about how far or how high he can jump; how much he can lift; how fast he can carry, punch or knock a ball.

But, if he produces a worthy thought or attempts to enunciate a mental process, or happens to evolve an original bit of intelligence, he must do so with a hacking cough and by dropping his head in abject modesty.

Sometimes, to illustrate an original thought, one finds it necessary to quote some other source for authority; you know, "Emerson said so-and-so." This to avoid any show of personal intelligence.

If a young person should have a tendency to express an opinion, bordering on original thought, all those around him wink and apologize for his inexperience. They will say, "Oh, he is a little opinionated but as he grows up it will wear off."

And, it probably will. He will be so circumvented by the lack of acceptance, that he will be sufficiently discouraged and will turn his prowess to something requiring the use of a ball or a pair of tennis shoes.

An excellent example of a person who excels in both the mental and physical fields is Paul Anderson of Vidalia. He has a brilliant mind and is an outstanding speaker; as well, he has lifted more dead weight than any other man in history.

He has established Paul Anderson Youth Homes and is widely known for his work in that field. Guess what he will be remembered for in the history books: his weightlifting.

Those who kick or knock balls may be recompensed in the thousands or millions of dollars.

Those whose field is training or stimulating the human mind are usually paid a bare living — or not quite.

Admit that you have long since learned to cultivate that proper hangdog look when you are cornered into any show of intelligence. By all means, be careful. It might be a fatal thing to become known as "bookish" or "intellectual."

If it does become necessary, and there is no other way out, don't lay on your listeners anything of an abstract or serious nature. To illustrate your point, quote some wit or comedian, so that your audience may giggle a little.

Really, it is better to stay with the glories of the ball or the killing of game while clinking the ice cubes with elbow bent, and, if perchance you stray, there is always the TV.

But, for heaven's sake, don't get caught thinking.

Up to No Good

Yes, your honor, this man was caught walking in the woods. Alone ... with no gun for hunting ... no tackle for fishing ... just walking and looking. Said he was looking at the flora and fauna, whatever that is. Up to no good, we say.

His name? Thoreau, Henry David. He refused, at first, to give his name. Said it was his "to give or to keep." Said he had no trade. Finally admitted that he sometimes helps his family make pencils. Likely story!

Judge to Officer: Does he have a criminal record?

Officer: Of a sort, your honor. He spent a night in the Concord Jail for refusing to pay a head tax. He didn't like the way the tax money was used. His friends paid the tax and he was released.

Judge: Mr. Thoreau, do you have any friends to vouch for you?

Thoreau: Judge, if I required vouching, I would not be worthy of the few I might name.

Judge: I remember you now, Mr. Thoreau. You seem to have slipped out of your time slot. You are more than a hundred years out of synchrony. A hundred years ago you might have been able to get by wandering in the woods, but not now. With no evidence that you intend to slaughter fish or fowl, you incite suspicion. For your own safety, you should be warned that you might be attacked by wild dogs, or bitten by a snake, or that you might break a leg in a gopher hole.

Thoreau: Your honor, I am grateful for your solicitude, but be advised that I am long since beyond these trepidations. I never do anything without purpose. I am here because this generation must be reintroduced to the simple act of walking.

I once bet a man that I could walk 30 miles before he could attain the same distance by conveyance. It was necessary for me to remind him that he first must employ himself for a time necessary to earn his carriage. This time, added to the trip, put me there first with time to spare.

The lesson is this: with your current shortage of fuel and the high cost of these automotive contraptions, much of your travel could be better done, and more economically accomplished, with your feet.

Judge: Sir, your point is well taken. I hope you get your message across. Thank you for coming. And, will you please give our best regards to Mr. Emerson and Mr. Hawthorne.

Judge to Officer: Release Mr. Thoreau near a pond called Walden.

Thoreau: Good day, gentlemen. If you don't mind, I'd rather walk.

Does Bigger Mean Better?

For a long time there has been a trend toward "bigness" in almost everything, from ambitions to institutions, from the large economy size to the sprawl of cities. All things must grow constantly larger to follow the creed of those who believe bigger is better. From the chest to the Chesterfield, everything's got to be king size.

Consolidation is killing off all the small schools. One wonders: Is it not possible that true education might come easier in smaller institutions where the teacher knows each student and perhaps his parents?

Is it not possible that the incentive to be outstanding in one's own community is greater than it might be among a thousand strangers?

Committees, clubs and organizations comply with the creed of bigness. The process runs in a circle. The organization decides to employ a paid secretary in the expectation that he can swell the ranks of its membership. He does so and most of the organization's increased revenue goes to pay his own salary.

It then appears that with the help of an assistant the membership can be further increased to take care of those increased costs. By this process, in due course, you have a busy headquarters which devotes most of its time to raising money and most of the money to expanding itself.

There are some signs that "reverse English" is being applied to this process: Cities are choking themselves to death and are breaking up into suburban shopping and living areas. Many people are seeking the less congested zones.

All roads no longer lead to the big cities. People are seeking out the byways in preference to the highways. There are those who are revisiting the charm of a country lane, a picket fence and known neighbors.

In the effort toward improvement let's hope that we may learn to "cling to that which is good" and not lose it while grabbing at something merely larger.

13

THREE NIGHT SETTIN' UP

... It was quite often, in the days of great distances and slow traffic, to have a two-night all-night settin' up. But, generally, it was a rare occasion when it was necessary to have a three nighter ...

Three-Night Settin' Up

Everyone is aware it was once the custom to accord a deceased brother or sister at least a one-night all-night settin' up. It was quite often, in the days of great distances and slow traffic, to have a two-night all-night settin' up. But, generally, it was a rare occasion when it was necessary to have a three-nighter.

Of course, except for those who grieved greatly, settin' up with the deceased was not all bad. At least one table was filled with platters and plates of chicken and cake and other goodies. And, there were drinks both passive and potable to quench the late-night thirst.

There was the case of an elderly gentleman who had grown old in the service of a local lumber yard at the going rate of less than $1 per day. He had lived a clean, proper and upright life, mainly because his daily stipend did not permit riotous living.

It was at the time Uncle Sam finally got around to paying the old soldiers their "bonus." Our subject received a check for several hundred dollars, which was exactly several hundred dollars more than he had ever seen before.

He immediately dropped out of the lumber profession, bought him a second-hand Ford, several bottles of homemade liquor, enlisted the aid of some of the local single ladies and proceeded to sample the finer things of life. Not being accustomed thereto, (it was noted by all) "hit kilt him."

His liquor, the ladies and his money all sort of ran out — together. When the undertaker entered the picture, he was stone-cold dead and stone-cold broke at the same time.

This presented a dilemma.

The undertaker was reluctant to handle the matter on credit or on installment. Application was made to the government to "please send his burial allowance." You know how that red-tape business is. It took almost a week.

The first night's settin' up was in the usual manner. No problem. But, the second night, the gathered — friends and beloved — got a little tired and they later explained they felt there would be no harm in having a little toddy to help keep them awake. But, the third night, they further explained that some of the brothers and sisters felt there wouldn't be any harm in pushing the casket of the departed into a back room and clear the front room so those who might wish, could play the Victrola and dance a little.

At a late hour, the word of a "frolic" got to the ears of the local constabulary. Some of the neighbors about a mile up the road had complained of the noise.

Rising to the occasion, the chief of police bethought himself of an appropriate method of breaking up the proceedings.

He slipped a sheet over his head and climbed in a

back window. When he walked slowly into the festive room, it was said every exit was placed into use, and two or three made exits where none had previously existed.

When the guv'ment money finally arrived, the undertaker found it necessary to draft friends and employees to compose a decent crowd for a proper funeral.

Hornswoggling the Gypsies

T ribes of Gypsies used to travel over the countryside by horse and wagon. Their principle occupation was trading and selling horses and mules. They would usually camp in a location convenient to the county seat. As soon as the word got out, people would come from miles around to "trade with the Gypsies."

Finding a location to camp was sometimes difficult, because the Gypsies did not enjoy the very best of reputations.

My grandfather set aside a field the Gypsies could use. He enjoyed a sort of armed-truce friendship with the chief of a clan called the Sherlocks. He enjoyed their annual visit and took special pride in holding his own with the chief in his trades.

Grandpa always had a mule or horse with some deficiency or behavioral fault he had groomed and fattened up so he could "out-trade" Chief Sherlock.

The Chief, no doubt, allowed Grandpa to have his

little sport, knowing full well his host would spend the next 12 months grinning and telling about how he "hornswoggled old Sherlock."

Let it be noted that "out-trading" somebody in a horse trade after all the necessary truth was told did not constitute ethical fraud in those days. It was a kind of sport. A fellow gained standing in the community if he could out-trade a Gypsy.

For many years, Grandpa and Chief Sherlock took turns in getting the better of each other. One year Grandpa would smoulder at being taken, another year he would brag about out-tradin' the Gypsies.

The friendly rivalry continued until Grandpa traded off a blaze-faced pony with some blemish in his physique or character for which he enjoyed a year of superiority in such matters.

Alas, the Gypsies had to find them another place to camp after Chief Sherlock traded the same bad apple back to Grandpa one year later.

Grandpa didn't know he had been taken until after the first rain. The Chief had dyed the blaze spot and it didn't show up until the first hard rain and the Chief was in other territory.

Grandpa had to admit, "I've been hornswoggled," which was considerably worse than being "out-traded."

It took two or three seasons before Chief Sherlock and his clan were allowed back on the old campground.

Henry's Solution

O ld Henry lived by the side of the road that came into the little town. He had a pig or two in his backyard and a flock of chickens which wandered all over his yard and out into the road.

Henry was agitated off and on by the usual things that bother people in his price class. There was, however, one thing that would throw him into a vocal frenzy beyond all else; that was the disaster that struck regularly when his wayward chickens got scattered by one of those big, slick automobiles.

He usually knew the car and the driver, because it was often a repeat performance. When it happened, Henry started shaking his fist and cussing at the driver. He would drop whatever he was doing and follow the car on down to the store-fronts, damning and threatening lawsuits and other dire things. The driver of the car knew Henry. He would laugh at him and invite him to do his worst — whatever.

Each uprising would gradually subside until the next episode.

Henry's final solution became an example for cases of frustration to be told and retold for several miles around.

One morning, one of the leading citizens, who also happened to be one of the leading bootleggers, came sailing through old Henry's flock, scattering and maiming. Henry followed the car as usual, alternately running and jumping in his indignation. He called the driver by name while shaking his fist in his face:

"Jim, I have decided that there is just one thing for me to do about you all speeding by my house and killing my chickens. I have tried warning you; I've tried suing you and you don't pay any attention. You are still scattering and killing my chickens. I have finally come to the conclusion that there is just one thing for me to do."

"What's that, Mr. Henry?"

"And that's for me to keep my damn chickens out of the road."

The Phantom Professor

Everyone knows there are no such things as ghosts. Natural laws will not support such beings. The only rule that might suggest their existence is the corollary to the fact that anything a human can desire, does exist. The opposite must be true: anything one can dread or fear, must also exist.

But, certainly, there are no ghosts.

Well, perhaps there may be a few exceptions. Most people dread being alone in the dark. Spider webs, bats, etc. are unwelcome; things which are there when they ought not to be; things which should be there but are not; things which are either or neither when they appear to be ...

Well, it can become complicated, but you must be the judge:

In a setting of large oaks, hanging with gray moss, there was once located a small rural college. There were three buildings, each two stories high. One building was for classrooms.

One building was for the girls' dorm, plus the residence of the president and his family and the meager administrative offices.

The other building was the boys' dorm. One professor lived on each floor as monitor and counselor. Other instructors lived out in town with their families.

But, there seemed to be a third professor and a third floor in the boys' dorm. The third floor was where many things happened. Residents of each floor would claim that any unruly affairs or unwanted noises emanated from "the other floor." In addition to these expected allusions, there was another unexplained and unexplainable element: In the middle of the night, when everyone was quiet, "the phantom professor" could be heard coming up the stairsteps and down the corridor.

The disquieting thing, in addition to his never being seen, was that he could be heard climbing two sets of stairs when only one existed, and, with his walking cane, he could be heard walking down two corridors, one of which just could not be.

Awakened students listened to every step. In fact, they counted every step with the cover over their heads. They knew the number of steps leading up to the quiet squeak of his room-door hinges — on the extra floor which was not there.

Those who were brave enough would whisper, "there goes the professor."

Everyone knew about "the professor" and the stairs and the dorm floor which didn't exist. The president and the faculty knew, but they dismissed the subject casually, obviously to prevent giving the little college a bad image.

Once a small group of students decided to investigate beyond the obvious. They had heard a ghost would leave footprints if he walked through blood. So, at a late and lonely hour, they poured a bucket of slaughterhouse blood at the head of the stairs and vowed to use the tracks to determine the extent of the professor's nightly walks.

The entire dorm listened at midnight to the approaching footsteps and the bump, bump of the walking cane.

He got to the top of the creaky stairs. Everyone heard when he stepped in the blood; everyone heard when he slipped and fell; everyone heard the clatter of his cane.

No one missed the groan and the mutter as he pulled himself up.

Finally the steps resumed their way up the stairs which were not there and down the corridor which didn't exist. No one missed the creak of his door.

There was little sleep the remainder of the night. The committee of ghost catchers waited for dawn. Every student was on hand to be among the first to see the trail of the bloodstained footprints and to follow it to the end.

Gentle reader, pull up your cloak around your ears and remember natural laws are always in effect. Except, perhaps, in this case.

When the students looked at the head of the stairs where they had poured the bucket of slaughterhouse blood — there was no sign of blood, no evidence of footprints — nothing whatever.

Many of those who were there have sworn they heard the tapping of a cane and a muttered curse from the unknown area.

You, dear reader, must be admonished: there is no evidence of a phantom professor nor a lasting curse, but it is a fact the little college has faded away. The students, the instructors and the dorms are all gone. Even now, if you are brave enough to go there at midnight, you may hear the phantom professor walking endlessly down the corridors of time, upstairs over a vacant lot.

14

HOW ARE THINGS IN STUMPY POINT?

Once, we drove considerably out of the way to visit a remote, small community in North Carolina named Stumpy point. We did so in order to astound friends by saying, "Have you every been to Stumpy Point, North Carolina?"

When I Owned the City Gate

Because I have known and loved our oldest city, St. Augustine, Florida, for its last half-century, perhaps I may be forgiven for a few memories entwined therewith.

I used to *own* the famous old City Gate. For about five or six years, between my ages of 8 and 13, I lived in the beautiful and ancient town. Several little friends and I divided up the city. The Old Fort belonged to one; the Oldest House to another; the Narrowest Street to another; and I had the City Gate.

To *own* a place meant that you had the exclusive use of it from which to sell city maps, magnolia blossoms (in season) and to dispense information and directions to the tourists. The last sometimes elicited a 10 cent tip, but more often a thank-you grunt.

I do not recall that we were in the least delinquent in the current understanding of the term. We were, on the whole, helpful to the visitors.

To strict constructionists, we did *steal* the magnolias. We didn't think of it as stealing. The beautiful old magnolia trees were part of the publicly-owned park system. They belonged to everybody, especially to anybody that could climb a tree, and who could climb a tree better than a 10-year-old boy?

We knew we weren't supposed to pick those blooms. We never understood why. We were making the tourists happy, and, incidentally, making a dime. We felt that it beat letting the magnolias fade on the trees, unloved. It was work, climbing the trees. We believed we were earning our money and filling a need.

The only fly in the ointment were the policemen whose business it was to walk slowly from one end of the long street to the other and shoo little boys away from the trees.

They were kindly policemen. We understood one another. We watched for their slow approach. We seldom embarrassed them by having to be reprimanded. They understood that we were helping with the tourist trade. Quite often we ran errands for them.

It was a much slower pace then. The speed cops rode bicycles — the pedal kind.

The City Gate was not considered to be as important as the Old Fort, but I loved it and knew every crevice and crack in it. I kept the surrounding grass plot uncluttered and the trash removed. It was really *my gate*. Not just to exploit, but to protect.

Today, after 60 years, there is a new and better road through the city, which is much faster. But on that new road you miss a lot, including the Gate.

I always take the old street. I have to go by and see if my property is still intact.

They Never Let On

Occasionally, I have written of my grand-parents who lived between the 1850s and the 1930s. Perhaps I have mentioned that they migrated from the rolling hills of east-middle Georgia down to the wiregrass country. The distance of that move was less than 75 miles, but the time taken was several days.

When I was between the ages of 8 and 12, my grandmother told me:

"We moved with ox-carts, carrying our household belongings and personal possessions. Most of the time, we walked. We tried to follow near the creeks and rivers to get water for cooking and drinking. The women and children slept in the carts on the bedding; the men, under the carts on leaves and grass. We washed clothes and bathed in the creeks.

"We followed the few roads that existed and the trails when we could find them. Sometimes there were no trails and we traveled over open fields.

"Several times a cart would turn over and our belongings, which were packed in barrels, would fall out and roll down a hill."

In listening, it bothered me that things spilled out might have been broken. In answer to that, my grand-mother went over to the sideboard, where she kept what we called the dainty things, and showed me a beautiful little cup with the handle broken off. She said that was the only thing broken on the entire trip.

My paternal grandparents had never been more

than 75 miles from home until they were about 75 years old. Then my father took them to Florida where they saw, for the first time, palm trees, palmettos and the Atlantic Ocean. They saw big bridges, big buildings and many wonderful things.

They *didn't let on* that they *had never been anywhere*. They kept their dignity, and very few around them suspected what was going through their minds.

(I know it is presumptuous to write at such lengths about my grandparents, but I believe there may be many others in my age group who have similar memories.)

Gonna be Some Changes Made

I t is said that if you want to see how much you will be missed when you die, you should stick your finger in a bucket of water, then withdraw it. The hole your finger leaves will indicate the degree of your importance.

I don't know about all that ... but, I'll tell you one thing ...

When I am gone, somebody else is going to have to learn to empty ash trays in cars; pick up stray pieces of scrap paper from floors and lawns; straighten out gem clips; mark things in papers and magazines that other people ought to read; turn off lights, water and electric motors; throw away used paper cups and old napkins; ask if letters have been answered yet and why not; put venetian blind cords back in their sockets; take the mail to the post office; and other items of importance.

Somebody else will have to answer the phone after it has rung four or five times, so I can go get whoever it was that was too slow in getting there in the first place.

One fellow I know, who felt his family and friends might soon be growing fonder in his absence, went to see his doctor. When he got back, they asked him, "What did the doctor say?"

"Well, he said I am doing just fine, but he did say that he didn't think it would be worthwhile for me to start any continued stories."

This reminds me that somebody else is going to have to take my place, worrying about business — mostly other peoples'.

Somebody has got to replace me in taking up for the president when all those commentators badmouth him.

Lastly, there will be the matter of the national post office deficit that is going to follow my demise when they have to return or stop all that junk mail I've been getting.

Buddy, you watch; when I go, there will be some changes made.

How are Things
In Stumpy Point?

Most memories are made of small things.

I had a good friend, the late Whit Blount, with whom I used to travel for pleasure. We and our wives took trips to the mountains, to the low country of North Carolina, to New Orleans, to Florida and to most of the southeastern states.

I don't recall that we ever did or saw anything really spectacular. Of course, we saw the mountains and the seashore and other great natural and manmade wonders.

I recall vividly only a few distinct images of those travels:

In New Orleans, we were bored with and walked away from the famous French Quarter and sat on the banks of the Mississippi River and threw rocks in the water just to see them splash (like another idle-minded fellow named Tom Sawyer).

Another time, Whit said if you find yourself in a disappointing restaurant, always order a toasted cheese sandwich. It is hard to mess up a cheese sandwich.

We were in such a restaurant in south Florida. It was supposed to be *great*, but it wasn't. I leaned over and whispered, "What are you gonna eat?" I knew the answer before he said it: "A toasted cheese sandwich."

Once, we drove considerably out of the way to visit a remote, small community in North Carolina named

Stumpy Point. We did so in order to be able to astound friends by saying, "Have you ever been to Stumpy Point, North Carolina?" (Believe it or not, the very first friend I asked had been there and was well acquainted with it.)

But, through the years, when the conversation lagged, Whit or I would ask the other, "How you reckon things are getting along in Stumpy Point?"

Another time his talents for observation furnished entertainment.

We were riding through the low country of North Carolina when he observed that almost every home in the country, great or small, sported two rows of collards. Apparently, these two rows had the bottom leaves cropped to furnish the only green vegetables, most of the year. There was seldom one row or three rows. Just why there were two rows, no matter how long or short, would furnish reason for further study, no doubt.

But, when memories come up of the high points of travels with my late friend, Whit, I forget about all the great scenery. I see us tossing rocks in the Mississippi, ordering cheese sandwiches in Florida and counting rows of collards in North Carolina.

Or, wondering how things are in Stumpy Point.

I can hear Whit now chuckling across the way.

The Last of Five

Sometime between 1936 and 1941 I had the good fortune to come upon a historical circumstance that makes one of the most interesting little stories I can recall.

One day, the local physician stuck his head in my office door and told me there were two old ladies on the Warrenton road who wanted to tell me about their father who fought in the Revolutionary War, and that I had better hurry and go see them — they were not going to be here very long.

The-Revolutionary-War bit passed over me and registered as the Civil War, and since Civil War stories were plentiful, I went as a matter of courtesy and not out of any enthusiasm.

The two elderly ladies lived in a little farmhouse a few miles above Gibson. The front room was the living room and bedroom. One lady invited me in, the other was lying in bed and was unable to speak. She blinked her eyes at me in greeting. The other invited me to have the only chair. I declined and offered to sit on a camel-back trunk by the window.

To open the conversation, I said, "The doctor tells me that your father fought in the Civil War." She immediately corrected me: "No, the Revolutionary War — you know, with General Washington." She pointed at the gun above the little mantel. It was a flint-loader as used in that war.

She further explained that her father was almost 90 years old when they were born; that he had married a young woman in his old age and they were born from that marriage. She further explained that she and her sister were almost 90 years old, themselves. She gave the exact years, which I can no longer remember.

She said her father was a drummer boy and was present with General Washington when the English General Cornwallis surrendered at Yorktown in 1781. She let me take the gun down and look at it.

I asked her how they lived. She answered that they got $15 a month from the Daughters of the American Revolution. I don't know whether she meant the two together received $15 a month or that both got $15 each. She said a cousin, who lived down the road about a quarter of a mile came to see them every day and helped them out. She told me, in some detail, about her father's service as researched by the DAR organization.

I went back into town and found the doctor. We got pencil and paper and started counting: If their father was about 15 years old at Yorktown in 1781, that would mean he was born about 1766, which would mean that he had to be nearly 90 when the girls were born and that they would have room to be over 85 in 1940. Now, whether he was 85 and they 90, I don't remember.

The big question I planted on the doctor was this — was it possible that a man nearly 90 could father children with a young woman?

He said it was possible, and it happened often enough that it could not be legally questioned.

I went into military service late in 1941 and lost touch. After the war, I learned that the sister I saw in bed that day had died a few weeks after my visit, and that the other sister died a little later.

The Daughters of the American Revolution had presided at their funeral and had erected a monument at the spot. I understand that it can be seen there now.

The sisters were named Poole; I am sorry I don't recall their first names.

I later checked with authorities of the DAR and found that the Poole sisters were TWO of the last FIVE recognized actual daughters of soldiers who fought England for the freedom of this country.

There, in the lifetime of two actual generations, was the history of the United States. And, I could place my hand on the soldier's flint-lock rifle.

A few months later, the opportunity had passed, and the only contact would be to read about it.

My point is this — historical matters of interest are passing out of view every day; it behooves us all to keep a watchful eye and help to capture these connections before it is too late.

15

POLITICS: THE GREATEST SPORT

It's not baseball, or football, or golf or any of the running, jumping, hitting or knocking games. The most popular sport in this country is politics.

Politics: The Greatest Sport

It's not baseball, or football, or golf or any of the running, jumping, hitting or knocking games. The most popular sport in this country is politics.

Some people are candidates; some are full-time supporters; some play out on the fringes and others just stand over in the corner and act as Monday Morning Quarterbacks. The great majority of folks hold down that last position.

Of course, there are some who play more than one position. Many people will help defeat a candidate, which results in the final election of someone else, then they immediately flip over and serve in the position of critic of the candidate that survived.

We U.S. citizens are different from voters in most countries of the world; most of us barely get involved enough to go vote ... usually, only a little more than half of the qualified will bother to vote, and a big percentage of those who vote, do so in order to express their opposition rather than in enthusiastic support.

Voters in other countries go to two extremes; some are ardent supporters and after the public servant is elected, he is highly respected. He is elevated in the eyes of his constituency; often he is decorated with gold medallions and purple ribbons and all stand in respect when in his presence. He is generally permitted to serve without great criticism and is accorded the benefit of every doubt.

Of course, in some countries the other extreme prevails and the poor fellow is assassinated.

The peculiar behavior of the average citizen in this country may be ascribed to the fact that we formed this country with dissidents and critics from all the countries of the world.

Our ancestors generally came here because they couldn't get along with the political or religious powers in their original country. They may have gotten one of those little genes crossed up and now have something in their composition that causes them to cuss the establishment as a basic part of their nature.

Have you noticed, most people don't want to go to the trouble of trying to correct a situation? All they want is to find out who to cuss.

Many fine citizens, with good reputations, offer their services as Mayor, Councilman, County Officer, District Officer, etc. If they win, the populace will allow them about 30 days grace. Then, immediately, they will start criticizing them for all suggestions or actions.

Usually, as they serve and when their terms are up, they are looked upon as fools or scoundrels or both, until they have been out of office for a short while, after which their former good reputation gradually comes back. If they withdraw from any participation in public matters, they will resume their respected place in the community.

Ole 'Gene and His Followers

Almost 50 years ago, the most magnetic figure in Georgia politics was Eugene Talmadge, father of former Senator Herman Talmadge. It is difficult for present generation folks to comprehend the attraction a public figure like Talmadge was in those days. There was no television, not even all homes had radios. Communications was limited.

Politics was on a personal basis. You hitched up a wagon or cranked up a Ford and went for miles to see the man, hear him speak and, if you were persistent, push through the crowd to speak to him and shake his hand. The slightest acquaintance could be parlayed into a lifelong, first-name friendship.

If Ole Gene happened to say a few words to a group in your presence, his words were quickly translated into a direct quote — "Ole Gene told ME ..."

Gene was usually brown as a nut and wore horn-rim glasses. His dark, unruly hair gave him a calculated roughshod look. Although he managed — whether intended or not — to have his clothes look disheveled, a closer look would have found him well-dressed, sometimes dapper.

He exuded a rustic manner and an eternal pugnacity that made him the personal champion of an electorate that, in that day and time, felt otherwise abandoned. He excited great loyalty and quite a bit of bitter opposition. He told the folks, from the steps of every courthouse in Georgia, that they had only three friends — God Almighty, Sears-Roebuck and Eugene Talmadge.

They were convinced.

A lot of jokes were told on Talmadge, but they had to be friendly. A critical word could start a fight or break up a lifelong friendship.

A crossroads storekeeper once told this little story:

"I was doing a good business in my store, furnishing the farmers with their goods, supplies and fertilizer. I was doing about $100,000 in business each year (which would be equal to about a million dollars today).

"I didn't like Talmadge and one day, in the heat of the moment, I told a group of farmers, who I considered my neighbors and friends, that anybody who voted for Talmadge was a plain damn fool.

"None of them said anything. They just quietly walked out. To make a long story short, my business suddenly dropped to $15,000 for the year, and I had to close the store."

Gene was a master at keeping important folks in country counties "lined up." If he heard that a country courthouse official was "agin him" he would win him over, or some of Gene's local supporters would see that the official had opposition of his own at the next election. It was known as "keeping him occupied."

This one case happened in a small county Ole Gene was visiting. He heard that the Judge of the Ordinary was against him and there was nothing he could do or say that would do any good. Gene happened up on the judge in the hall of the courthouse. They greeted each other and Gene leaned over to the judge, who he could see by the corners of his mouth used chewing tobacco, and said, "Judge, would you happen to have a little chew of tobacco you'd loan a fellow?"

The judge, of course, rushed to be hospitable. He handed over his plug of Brown Mule. Gene took it while the judge was fishing for his pocket knife for Gene to use to cut a corner. To clinch the matter, Gene asked, "Judge, do you mind if I just bite it?" The judge fell over himself to agree.

Gene thanked the judge, as one tobacco chewer to another, with the same degree of gratitude reserved for momentous events.

And the judge wrapped the remainder of that plug in brown paper and saved it, perhaps for the rest of his life. He would take it out and show it to anybody who had time to listen, tell the story and say, with deep emotion, "Ole Gene bit off my plug."

It is needless to say Ole Gene enjoyed his friendship right on into eternity.

And then this little story about Ole Gene speaks volumes:

First Georgian: They gonna move Stone Mountain.

Second Georgian: Man, nobody can move Stone Mountain.

First Georgian: Ole Gene says he's gonna move it.

Second Georgian: Shonuff? Where's he gonna put it?

It's 'One of These Days'

E verybody has been saying it for years — "one of these days there has got to be a reckoning. The government can't keep on throwing away tax money like it is."

Democrats, Republicans, Hotentots, whatever ... everybody knew that sooner or later we were going to have to quit doing as we were doing and take our medicine.

And everybody used to say, "Nobody is going to like it if he has to be cut loose from a sugar plum, but this thing has got to be straightened out, sooner or later."

Now isn't that so?

Well, we are now living in *these days*. As President Reagan's axe falls, you can hear the weepin' and the wailin', just like everybody said.

People who want to criticize — but don't want to cuss — the president are blaming everything on Reaganomics.

Why just t'other day I heard of this fellow:

He got to noticing things. You know, like his telephone number. It was 444-4444. His house number and address. He lived at No. 44 Fourth Avenue, in the 4th Ward of the city. He said to himself, "Man, what a set-up. Here I live at 44 Fourth Avenue in the 4th Ward, my telephone number is 444-4444, and it just happens that there is a race horse, No. 44 in the fourth race, paying 4-1. Man, I can't lose."

He sat down to his telephone (number 444-4444) at his home (at 44 Fourth Avenue in the 4th Ward) and called his bookie. He said, "Put $400 on No. 44 in the fourth race, paying 4-1."

He quietly waited for his bookie to call him back. At exactly 4 p.m. that day, his phone rang. As he waited expectantly, the bookie said, "No 44 in the fourth race, paying 4-1, finished fourth."

He slammed the receiver down and said, "To hell with Ronald Reagan."

Back Up Your Wagon

I n recent years, we have seen one U.S. Senator, four or five congressmen, eight or 10 mayors and county commissioners and several sheriffs succumb to the temptation of *under the table* inducements.

Such instances have served to provide further *proof* to many unthinking people that all public officials are bad and that all politicians are crooked.

There must be well over 2,000 people in Georgia alone serving as mayors, councilmen, county commissioners and in other elected offices. A great majority serve without pay, or receive only a small travel or gasoline allowance. Most of these people serve only because of devotion to their communities and in an effort to contribute to the welfare and growth of those communities. Many serve at considerable inconvenience and expense to themselves.

Out of 100 senators and several hundred congressmen, about a half dozen were *abscamed* a few years ago. That's not good, but the percentage is not bad. It is better than one might find in many other trades or professions.

Some sincere citizens are misled to believe the worst of politicians because the very small percentage of bad ones are given so much publicity. There is another motive for some of the criticism — however unconscious. Some critics believe the worst of those who handle public money because they know what they would do if they could get their hands in the public trough.

In any case, public servants believe that the best cure for political distrust is to run for or accept appointment to some public office.

They say, "Back your wagon up and get it loaded down with public responsibility. It is not likely that you will accomplish all the things you would like, but you will find it highly educational." And, they say, "You will find many more crooks outside than in office."

Roosevelt and the Presidents

Wouldn't it be a spectacle to see all the presidents since Roosevelt assembled in a group with the great Franklin D.?

Of course, Roosevelt would be the center of attention. He would be the leader, recognized by all.

Harry Truman would be standing very erect in the presence of his commander-in-chief and alertly awaiting any orders or suggestions.

Dwight Eisenhower would be, more properly, wearing his Eisenhower Jacket uniform and alternately looking off in the distance while listening very intently.

John F. Kennedy would be leaning against Roosevelt's wheelchair in an attitude of old-school camaraderie, with an occasional reference to Harvard.

Richard Nixon would be trying to interject a very, very serious question or comment about international affairs.

Roosevelt would ask Lyndon Johnson to go get him a pack of cigarettes, which Johnson would do with ostentatious dispatch.

Gerald Ford, while watching Roosevelt with awe, would be trying to whisper with Ike about golf.

Jimmy Carter would be standing as close to Roosevelt as he could get while beaming that thousand-watt smile.

Ronald Reagan would be explaining to "the chief" that he had no intention of undoing the New Deal program ... that he was only trying to tighten up on the waste and extravagance, and stop the government from trying to be "all things to all people."

Roosevelt would assure them that, with few exceptions, he thought they had all done a "dandy job."

He would tell Reagan: "My friend, don't allow yourself to be nibbled to death by ducks."

To the group he would say, "This great nation has survived foreign wars and civil strife; it has overcome the terrible years of devastating depression — and it will continue to prosper.

"It will withstand the ingratitude of those who have benefitted the most, and it will continue to provide for the lame, the halt and the blind. It will assist the old, the destitute and the needy. It will help in times of emergency and disaster among our own people, as well as our neighbors throughout the world.

"We must leave no room for the smallness and meanness in the nature of man. This nation is the wellhead of the great and the good.

"I have little patience with those who, through penury of spirit, say we cannot lend a helping hand."

Turning to Reagan, he would say, "Ron, you are correct in tightening the reins of administration. Our programs never intended waste and extravagance. Neither did we intend to substitute for the backbone of individual initiative.

"I tell you: there is a happy in-between — a middle way. I hope you find it."

And from the seriousness of the moment, with his cigarette holder pointed at two o'clock and his hat brim snapped up, he would smile the Roosevelt smile and, with a wave, leave the small group of men standing wide-eyed, with their mouths hanging open.